Multiple Questions

on

Advanced Level Mathematics

R. W. Payne
Third Master and Head of Mathematics
Dulwich College

D. B. Pennycuick
Head of the Mathematics Department
Chislehurst and Sidcup Grammar School

BELL & HYMAN
LONDON

Published by
BELL & HYMAN LIMITED
Denmark House
37–39 Queen Elizabeth Street
London SE1 2QB

First published in 1975 by
G. Bell & Sons Ltd
Reprinted 1976, 1978

ISBN 0 7135 1927 4

Printed in Great Britain at
The Camelot Press Ltd Southampton

Preface

Scope of the book. The questions in this book cover the London GCE Advanced Level syllabuses in Mathematics and Further Mathematics to be. examined from June 1977. In addition to candidates preparing for these examinations, the book should be useful to those taking A Levels of other boards and to teachers of mathematics in sixth forms and Colleges of Education.

Terminology and types. A multiple choice or *objective* question usually consists of a *stem* (brief preliminary information, often concluding with a question or incomplete statement) followed by a number of suggested answers, or *responses*. The correct response is called the *key* and the others are *distractors*. Our questions , or *items*, like those of the University of London, have four distractors and we have used the five item types which the University has adopted. These types, and the abbreviations used in this book to identify them, are :

Simple Multiple Choice	
Multiple Completion	**MC**
Relationship Analysis	**RA**
Data Necessity	**DN**
Data Sufficiency	**DS**

Arrangement of the book. Each item type is introduced, explained, and followed by a selection of examples on topics likely to be covered early in a sixth form course.

Questions 80-279 cover the Mathematics syllabus excluding Mechanics, and are arranged in groups, ten Multiple Choice items alternating with ten of the other four item types. Most of the harder questions occur later in the section but some easy ones are to be found throughout.

Questions 280-349 cover the Mechanics parts of the Mathematics syllabus. Again each group of twenty successive questions includes all of the item types.

Questions 350-549 are on the Further Mathematics syllabus, 350-479 being on Pure Mathematics, the rest on Mechanics and Statistics. These are followed by twenty harder questions, intended to be studied at leisure.

3

Notes on some of the questions appear at the end of the book together with an appendix on item writing and an index. A list of answers is available upon application to the publishers.

Use of the book. Objective questions not only provide a good way of consolidating ground-work and of refreshing the memory, they also form an excellent test of important logical concepts. We recommend that pupils be set questions to try in the first half of a period and that the rest of the time be spent in discussing the problems.

Marking objective tests. In common with other boards setting objective tests, London obtains a candidate's score by counting his correct responses, making no deduction for wrong answers and giving no allowance for questions not attempted. Consequently a candidate need feel no inhibition about answering an item in which his investigation has eliminated some of the suggested answers without pointing conclusively to the correct one. Indeed he should consider whether the last few moments of the examination would be better spent in giving answers to all of the questions which he has left out through lack of time or understanding or in trying to work out some of them.

Acknowledgements. We are grateful to our pupils on whom we have tried the questions and who have not been slow in pointing out weaknesses, and to the University of London Entrance and School Examinations Council who have allowed us to use their standard directions for each item type. In particular we thank their former Mathematics Subject Officer, Nigel Warwick, B.Sc., for his interest, encouragement and advice. We thank our publishers who have made many useful suggestions while leaving the decisions to us.

December, 1974   R.W.P.
                                                                    D.B.P.

Contents

Introduction to the item types

Simple multiple choice items

Each item consist of a problem followed by five suggested answers. The stem is normally complete in itself so that the problem can be understood without reading the answers. It is sometimes possible to arrive at the key by rejection of the alternatives but it is usually better to solve the problem directly.

Twenty Simple Multiple Choice questions follow: ten on Pure Mathematics, ten on Mechanics.

PAPER 1

10 If the line joining $(-3, 5)$ and $(3, -7)$ has equation $y = mx + c$, then c is

   A -13 **B** $-5\frac{1}{2}$ **C** -1 **D** $3\frac{1}{2}$ **E** 11

11 The exact value of $\cos 240°$ is

   A $\dfrac{\sqrt{3}}{2}$ **B** $\dfrac{1}{2}$ **C** 0 **D** $-\dfrac{1}{2}$ **E** $-\dfrac{\sqrt{3}}{2}$

12 The sum of 12 terms of the arithmetic series $-9, -5, -1, 3, \ldots$ is

   A 35 **B** 156 **C** 180 **D** 210 **E** 312

13 If $y = \dfrac{1}{3x^2}$ then $\dfrac{dy}{dx}$ is

   A $\dfrac{1}{6x}$ **C** $\dfrac{-6}{x^3}$ **E** $-\dfrac{1}{9x^4}$

   B $-\dfrac{2}{3x}$ **D** $-\dfrac{2}{3x^3}$

14 The sum of the squares of the roots of the equation $2x^2 + 5x + 1 = 0$ is equal to

   A $4\frac{1}{4}$ **B** $5\frac{1}{4}$ **C** $6\frac{1}{4}$ **D** 23 **E** 25

15 Find the area bounded by the curve $y = x^2 - 4x + 10$, the x-axis and the ordinates $x = 1$ and $x = 3$.

A 4 **B** $12\frac{2}{3}$ **C** 21 **D** $28\frac{2}{3}$ **E** $32\frac{2}{3}$

16 How many different combinations of three letters can be selected from the word ISOSCELES ?

A 7 **B** 20 **C** 31 **D** 84 **E** 151

17 Expressed as a product of factors,

$\sin(\alpha + \beta) - \sin(\alpha - \beta)$ is

A $2 \sin \beta \cos \beta$ **B** $2 \cos \alpha \cos \beta$ **C** $2 \sin \alpha \cos \beta$
D $2 \sin \alpha \sin \beta$ **E** $2 \cos \alpha \sin \beta$

18 The gradient of the parabola $x = 2t^2$, $y = 4t$ at the point $t = -2$ is

A -2 **C** $-\frac{1}{2}$ **E** 2
B -1 **D** $\frac{1}{2}$

19 If $\dfrac{5x}{(x+2)(x-3)} \equiv \dfrac{P}{x+2} + \dfrac{Q}{x-3}$, then

A $P = 2, Q = 3$ **C** $P = -2, Q = 3$ **E** P, Q are none of these.
B $P = 2, Q = -3$ **D** $P = -2, Q = -3$

PAPER 2

20

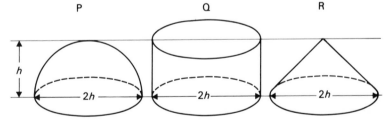

These uniform solids, a hemisphere, a right circular cylinder and a right circular cone, are placed side by side on a very rough horizontal plane. The plane is tilted until the solids fall. Assuming that they do not hit each other when they move, in what order do they fall ?

A P R Q **C** Q R P **E** R Q P
B Q P R **D** R P Q

21 Energy is measured in

A joules   **C** newtons   **E** watts
B kilograms   **D** newton-seconds

22

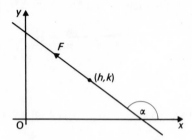

A force F acts as shown in the diagram. Its anticlockwise moment about O is

A $F(h \sin\alpha + k \cos\alpha)$ **C** $F(h \cos\alpha - k \sin\alpha)$ **E** $F(k \cos\alpha - h \sin\alpha)$
B $F(h \sin\alpha - k \cos\alpha)$ **D** $F(k \sin\alpha + h \cos\alpha)$

23 Elastic string P has twice the modulus and extension of elastic string Q but it has half the natural length of Q. If the energy stored in it is n times that in Q then n is

A 1   **B** 2   **C** 4   **D** 8   **E** 16

24

Before ——→ x w ←——

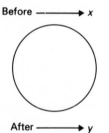

After ——→ y ——→ z

The coefficient of restitution between these directly impinging spheres is

A $\dfrac{z - y}{w + x}$ **C** $\dfrac{w + x}{y - z}$ **E** $\dfrac{y + z}{x - w}$

B $\dfrac{y - z}{w + x}$ **D** $\dfrac{x - w}{y + z}$

25 A particle moves in a straight line so that after t seconds its velocity is $(3t^2 - 2t + 4)$ ms^{-1}. How many metres does it travel in the fourth second ?

A 34 **C** 56 **E** 64
B 40 **D** 58

26 A ship is heading on a bearing $020°$ but as a result of a current from the NE her course is due N. If her speed in still water is 12 knots, which of the following triangles of velocities can be used to find her actual speed ?

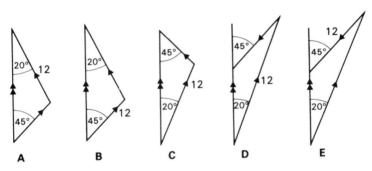

27 Distance being measured in metres, the initial position of a particle is $\mathbf{i} + 2\mathbf{j}$. The particle has constant velocity 10 ms^{-1} in the direction $3\mathbf{i} - 4\mathbf{j}$. What is its position after 2 seconds ?

A $4\mathbf{i} - 2\mathbf{j}$ **C** $12\mathbf{i} - 16\mathbf{j}$ **E** $61\mathbf{i} - 78\mathbf{j}$
B $7\mathbf{i} - 6\mathbf{j}$ **D** $13\mathbf{i} - 14\mathbf{j}$

28 In SI units a particle has momentum p and mass m. Express its kinetic energy in terms of p and m.

A $\dfrac{p}{m}$ **C** $\dfrac{p^2}{2m}$ **E** $\dfrac{p^2}{2m^2}$

B $\frac{1}{2}mp^2$ **D** $\frac{1}{2}mp$

29 A particle of weight W is suspended in equilibrium by two strings which are tied to the particle and which are perpendicular to each other. One string is inclined at α to the horizontal and the tension in it is T. Express W in terms of T and α.

A $T\sin\alpha$ **C** $T\sec\alpha$ **E** $T\sin\alpha\cos\alpha$
B $T\cos\alpha$ **D** $T\operatorname{cosec}\alpha$

Multiple Completion Items (MC)

Directions. In questions of this type, three responses are given, of which ONE or MORE are correct. Decide which of the responses is (are) correct. Then choose

A   if **1, 2** and **3** are correct
B   if only **1** and **2** are correct
C   if only **2** and **3** are correct
D   if only **1** is correct
E   if only **3** is correct

Summary of directions

A	B	C	D	E
1, 2, 3	**1, 2** only	**2, 3** only	**1** only	**3** only

The above table is used by the University of London. An alternative one is printed on the fold-out flap at the end of the book. This flap also gives summaries of the other item types.

Worked Example. An approximation for $\sqrt{3}$ can be obtained by using the first few terms of the binomial expansion of $(1+x)^{-1/2}$ in ascending powers of x and putting x equal to

1   2   **2** $\frac{1}{3}$ **3** $-\frac{1}{4}$

Response **1** is incorrect, since the expansion is not valid for $x = 2$.
If we put $x = \frac{1}{3}$, $(1+x)^{-1/2} = \frac{1}{2}\sqrt{3}$, and response **2** is correct.
If we put $x = -\frac{1}{4}$, $(1+x)^{-1/2} = \frac{2}{3}\sqrt{3}$, so that response **3** is also correct.
Hence the key is **C**.

Comments. Note that at least one of the responses must be correct. Since there are only five suggested answers, not all combinations of true and false responses can be covered. The reader may have noticed that in the worked example it was not necessary to consider response **3** once it had been decided that **1** was false. However to consider **3** provides a check.

In this book the clumsy " is (are) " has been avoided wherever possible. No significance should be attached to the use of a singular or a plural verb in the stem of a Multiple Completion item.

Twenty of these items follow.

PAPER 3

30
MC The curve with parametric equations

$$x = 1 + t, \ y = 1 + t^3$$

passes through the points

1 (0, 0) **2** (1, 1) **3** (2, 2)

31
MC The triangle with vertices $(-1, -2), (3, 1), (-4, 2)$

1 is isosceles **2** is right angled **3** has area 25

32
MC There is a solution of the equation $3 \cos \theta + 2 = 0$ in

1. quadrant 1 **2** quadrant 2 **3** quadrant 3

33
MC If the sum of the first n terms of an arithmetic series is equal to $3n + 2n^2$ then

1 the second term is 14 **2** the common difference is 3
3 the sum of the first three terms is 27

34
MC If $f(x) \equiv ax^2 + bx + c$ then $f(x + 1) - 2f(x) + f(x - 1)$ is independent of

1 x **2** b **3** c

35
MC If the circles $x^2 + y^2 = 4$ and $(x - 3)^2 + (y - 4)^2 = r^2$ touch each other, then r may be

1 7 **2** 3 **3** 1

36
MC If $\dfrac{3x^2 - 2x + 5}{(x^2 + x - 1)(x - 1)^2}$ is expressed as the sum of three partial fractions, which of the following denominators will have numerators dependent on x ?

1 $x - 1$ **2** $(x - 1)^2$ **3** $x^2 + x - 1$

37
MC The expression $\cos(\theta + \phi) + \cos\theta + \cos(\theta - \phi)$ vanishes when

1 $\theta = \pi/2$ **2** $\phi = 5\pi/6$ **3** $\theta = \phi = \pi$

38
MC A *perfect* number is a number equal to the sum of its divisors including 1 but excluding the number itself. Which of the following are perfect ?

1 16 **2** 28 **3** 6

39
MC Given that $ax^2 + 2bx + c > 0$ for all real values of x it follows that

1 $a > 0$ **2** $c > 0$ **3** $ac > b^2$

PAPER 4

40
MC Which of the following are vectors ?

1 momentum   **2** work   **3** kinetic energy

41
MC Linear acceleration can be expressed as

1 $\dfrac{dv}{dt}$ **2** $\dfrac{d^2x}{dt^2}$ **3** $\dfrac{vdv}{dx}$

42
MC A body of weight W rests in equilibrium on a plane inclined at an angle α to the horizontal. The coefficient of friction is μ.
The frictional force depends on

1 μ **2** α **3** W

43
MC The dimensions of a physical quantity are expressed in the form the form $M^\alpha L^\beta T^\gamma$. $\alpha + \beta + \gamma = -1$ for

1 momentum   **2** work   **3** acceleration

44
MC If a particle moves along the x-axis so that at time t
$x = t^3 - 9t^2 + 27t + 8$ then

    1 when $t = 3$ the velocity is zero
    2 when $t = 3$ the acceleration is zero
    3 when $t > 3$ the particle is at rest.

45
MC

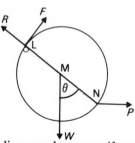

The diagram shows a uniform ring hanging in equilibrium over a rough peg and pulled aside by a horizontal force which is applied diametrically opposite to the peg. Which of the following moment equations are correct ?

    1   About L, $W\sin\theta = P\cos\theta$.
    2   About M, $F = P\sin\theta$.
    3   About N, $2F = W\sin\theta$.

46 Three forces are represented completely by $\overline{PQ}$, $\overline{QR}$ and $\overline{RS}$.
MC Their resultant

    1   has the magnitude of $\overline{PS}$
    2   has the direction of $\overline{PS}$
    3   acts along $\overline{PS}$.

47
MC

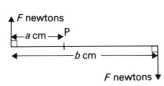

The moment of this system about P depends on the value of

    1 *a*   **2** *b*   **3** *F*

48
MC

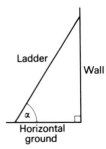

The ladder CANNOT rest in equilibrium as shown if

    1   the ground is smooth and the wall is rough
    2   the ground is rough and the wall is smooth
    3   the coefficients of friction with the wall and ground are equal.

49 The point of intersection of the medians of the triangle PQR is
MC necessarily coincident with the centre of mass of

    1   three equal particles at P, Q, R
    2   a uniform triangular lamina PQR
    3   a uniform wire bent to form the perimeter of triangle PQR.

13

Relationship Analysis Items (RA)

Directions
Items of this type consist of two statements (in some cases following brief preliminary information). You are required to determine the relationship between these statements and to answer

- **A**   if **1** always implies **2**, but **2** does not imply **1**
- **B**   if **2** always implies **1**, but **1** does not imply **2**
- **C**   if **1** always implies **2** and **2** always implies **1**
- **D**   if **1** always denies **2** and **2** always denies **1**
- **E**   if none of the above relationships holds.

Worked example
An infinite geometric series has common ratio r.
- **1**   The series is convergent.
- **2** $r < 1$

The condition for the convergence of a geometric series of common ratio r is $-1 < r < 1$. Hence **1** implies **2**, but as **2** is satisfied when $r < -1$, it is insufficient to ensure convergence. Hence the key is **A**.

The item may be made to have other keys by altering statement **2**.

If **2** is changed to $0 < r < 1$, then **2** does imply **1**. As there are other values of r for which the series converges, **1** does not imply **2** and the key is **B**.

If statement **2** were $-1 < r < 1$, the two statements would be equivalent and the key would be **C**.

Alternatively the item would have key **D** if statement **2** were $r > 1$, for each of the statements would then deny the other.

Finally, consider the situation when the second statement is $r > 0$. The series is convergent for some of the values of r which satisfy this condition but it is divergent for others. On the other hand statement **1** does not require that $r > 0$ so that none of the relationships **A**, **B**, **C**, **D** holds and the key is **E**.

Ten items of this type follow.

PAPER 5

50
RA
1 H is the orthocentre of triangle PQR.
2 P is the orthocentre of triangle HQR.

51
RA
1 $\cos 2\alpha = 0$ **2** $\cos \alpha - \sin \alpha = 0$

52
RA
1 $a - b > 0$ **2** $a^2 - b^2 > 0$

53
RA
1 There is a point of inflection at $(a, f(a))$ on the curve $y = f(x)$.
2 $f''(a) = 0$

54
RA
1 The graph of $\ln y$ against x is a straight line.
2 y and x satisfy a relationship of the form $y = ax^n$ where a and n are non-zero constants.

55
RA
1 $5 \cot \alpha = 13$
2 $5 \operatorname{cosec} \alpha = 12$

56
RA
p, q, r are positive.
1 $\ln p, \ln q, \ln r$ are in A. P.
2 p, q, r are in G.P.

57
RA
A particle moves in a straight line. t denotes the time in seconds.
1 Its velocity is $2\sin 3t$ ms^{-1} for all $t \geqslant 0$.
2 Its acceleration is $6\cos 3t$ ms^{-2} for all $t \geqslant 0$.

58
RA
A body of mass m is suspended in a lift by an inextensible string.
1 The magnitude of the tension in the string is $\dfrac{3mg}{4}$.
2 The magnitude of the acceleration of the lift is $\dfrac{g}{4}$.

59
RA
A body is acted on by just three forces.
1 The body is in equilibrium.
2 The forces are concurrent.

Data Necessity Items (DN)

Directions. Each of these questions consists of a problem followed by four pieces of information. Do not actually solve the problem, but decide whether the problem could be solved if any of the pieces of information were omitted, and choose

    A   if **1** could be omitted
    B   if **2** could be omitted
    C   if **3** could be omitted
    D   if **4** could be omitted
    E   if none of the pieces of information could be omitted.

Although the directions do not say so, it may be assumed that the four pieces of information are together sufficient to solve the problem.

Worked example. M is the mid-point of the chord $px + qy + r = 0$ of the circle $x^2 + y^2 = a^2$. Find the numerical value of the y co-ordinate of M.

    1 $a = 6$ **2** $p = 4$ **3** $q = 3$ **4** $r = -2$

Eliminating x between the two equations gives $(qy + r)^2 + p^2y^2 = p^2a^2$.
The y co-ordinate of M is given by half the sum of the roots of this quadratic in y, the expression for which involves p, q and r but not a. Hence the key is **A**.

    A shorter solution is obtained by noting that M is the foot of the perpendicular from the origin to the chord and its co-ordinates will be independent of a.

Comment. It is usually better to avoid approaching a problem by considering each piece of information in turn and deciding whether it can be left out. Items which require such a technique are not entirely satisfactory as the time taken to answer them will depend on the order in which the information is investigated. However, when this approach is adopted, a little initial thought may be profitable. For instance, if in the worked example both co-ordinates of M had been required, noting the complete symmetry between x and y in the question would have ruled out keys **B** and **C**.

    In our mechanics questions the value of g may not be assumed but its value is sometimes given as one of the four pieces of information. Here our practice differs from that of the University of London in whose papers the value of g may always be assumed. We think that the consideration of the relevance of g can be a significant one.

    This item type lacks some of the variety of others for there are essentially only two sorts of problems—those requiring all of the information for their solution and those from which one piece can be omitted.

    There follow ten Data Necessity items.

PAPER 6

60
DN
Evaluate $\dfrac{f(p)-f(q)}{p-q} - \dfrac{f(q)-f(r)}{q-r}$ where $f(x) \equiv ax^2$ and $p \neq q \neq r$.

1   $a = 3$ 3 $q = 2$
2   $p = 4$ 4 $r = 1$

61
DN
Does the equation $x^2 + 2hxy + by^2 + 2gx + c = 0$ represent a real circle ?

1   $b = 1$ 3 $g = 1$
2   $c = -1$ 4 $h = 0$

62
DN
$\alpha, \beta, \gamma, \delta$ being distinct, evaluate

$$\frac{\cos(\alpha + \beta) + \cos(\beta + \gamma)}{\cos(\gamma + \delta) + \cos(\delta + \alpha)} \cdot$$

1   $\alpha = \pi/6$ 3 $\beta = \pi/3$
2   $\alpha + \gamma = \pi/4$ 4 $\beta + \delta = \pi/2$

63
DN
Is $\triangle PQR \equiv \triangle XYZ$?

1   $\angle Q = \angle Y$ 3 $r = z$
2   $q = y$ 4   The triangles are acute angled.

64
DN
What is the probability that a ball drawn at random from a bag is black ?

1   All of the balls in the bag are either black, white or blue.
2   There are 170 black balls in the bag.
3   The ratio of the number of black balls to the number of white is 17 : 11.
4   The ratio of the number of blue balls to the number of white is 13 : 22.

65
DN
Find the numerical value of $\int_0^{\frac{\pi}{2}} (p \cos x + q \sin x + r \cos 2x + s \sin 2x)\, dx$.

1   $p = 1$ 3 $r = 2$
2   $q = -1$ 4 $s = -2$

66
DN
If $y = a \ln kx$, where a and k are constants, find an approximate value of δy.

1   $a = 0 \cdot 2$ 3 $kx = 0 \cdot 3$
2   $x = 3$ 4 $\delta x = 0 \cdot 01$

67
DN

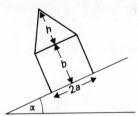

The diagram shows a solid cone joined to a cylinder of the same uniform density as the cone, the body resting on a very rough plane.
Will it topple ?

1 $\alpha = \pi/4$ **3** $b = 8\,\text{cm}$
2 $a = 4\,\text{cm}$ **4** $h = 6\,\text{cm}$

68
DN

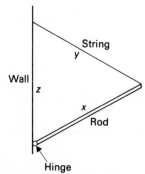

A uniform rod of weight 2 newtons is in equilibrium as shown.
Find the numerical value of the tension in the string.

1 $x = 0\cdot5\,\text{m}$ **3** $z = 0\cdot7\text{m}$
2 $y = 0\cdot8\,\text{m}$ **4** The hinge is smooth.

69
DN

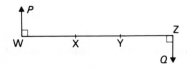

What is the numerical value of the moment of this system about X ?

1 X and Y are the points of trisection of WZ.
2 The moment of the system about X is equal to its moment about Y.
3 $P = 10\,\text{N}$ **4** WZ $= 90\,\text{cm}$

18

Data Sufficiency Items (DS)

Directions. Each question consists of a problem and two statements **1** and **2** in which certain data are given. You are not asked to solve the problem : you have to decide whether the data given in the statements are sufficient for solving the problem. Using the data given in the statements, choose

  A if EACH statement (i.e. statement **1** ALONE and statement **2** ALONE) is sufficient by itself to solve the problem

  B if statement **1** ALONE is sufficient but statement **2** is not sufficient to solve the problem

  C if statement **2** ALONE is sufficient but statement **1** is not sufficient to solve the problem

  D if BOTH statements **1** and **2** TOGETHER are sufficient to solve the problem, but NEITHER statement ALONE is sufficient

  E if statements **1** and **2** TOGETHER are NOT sufficient to solve the problem, and additional data specific to the problem are needed

Worked example 1. Does the equation $a \cos \theta + b = 0$ have a solution for θ in the second quadrant ?

  1 $a > b$
  2 $b > 0$

Considered in isolation neither statement is sufficient to ensure that the equation has any solutions, let alone one which lies in the required range. When taken in conjunction they imply that $\cos \theta$ lies between -1 and 0 so that there is a solution for θ in the range $\frac{\pi}{2} < \theta < \pi$, and the key is **D**. Note that in this case the answer to the question is YES. Had the question been

  " Does $a \cos \theta + b = 0$ have a solution in the fourth quadrant ? " the key would still have been **D**, for both statements would be required in order to answer the question, this time in the negative.

Worked example 2. Two particles of masses m, km are connected by a light inextensible string passing over a smooth fixed pulley. The parts of the string not in contact with the pulley are vertical. Given g, what is the numerical value of the acceleration of the mass m ?

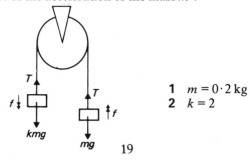

  1 $m = 0 \cdot 2 \text{ kg}$
  2 $k = 2$

19

The equations of motion are

$$kmg - T = kmf$$
$$T - mg = mf$$

On eliminating T the expression for f depends on k but not on m. Thus the key is **C**.

The item may be answered with less detailed analysis. It is apparent that the problem is a determinate one if both m and k are known. The dimensions of f are independent of M and so the expression for f will be independent of m, the only quantity with dimensions involving M.

Note that in neither method is it necessary to find f explicitly.

Comments. In writing Data Sufficiency items it is particularly important to give all of the relevant information intended. However, the reader should not be over meticulous in considering data. For instance, in the second worked example, we have not stated that air resistance is to be neglected, but key **E** is not intended.

The next paper consists of ten items of this type.

PAPER 7

70
DS

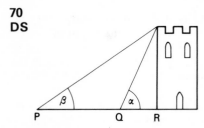

Given $\tan \alpha = 1 \cdot 5$ and $\tan \beta = 0 \cdot 8$ find the height of the tower.

1 PQ = 14 metres **2** QR = 16 metres

71 Find the value of $a + b$.
DS
1 $a^2 + b^2 = 25$ **2** $ab = 12$

72 OPQR is a rhombus, O being the origin. What are the coordinates of Q?
DS
1 The diagonal PR has equation $2x + 3y = 13$.
2 The diagonals OQ and PR meet at (2, 3).

73 Does $x^2 + 2hxy + y^2 + 2gx + 2fy + c = 0$ represent a real circle?
DS
1 $h = 0$ **2** $f^2 + g^2 < c$

74
DS Is the gradient of $y = \dfrac{ax}{x-b}$ positive at the origin ?

1 $a > 0$ **2** $b > 0$

75
DS P, Q have position vectors **p**, **q** respectively and a point X on PQ has position vector $\dfrac{\mathbf{p} + \lambda \mathbf{q}}{\mu}$. What is the numerical value of the ratio in which X divides PQ ?

1 $\lambda = 2$ **2** $\mu = 3$

76
DS Air is being blown into a spherical balloon at the rate of $15 \text{ cm}^3\text{s}^{-1}$. The radius of the balloon is r cm and its volume is V cm³. What is the rate of increase of the radius ?

1 $r = 10$ **2** $\dfrac{\mathrm{d}V}{\mathrm{d}r} = 400\pi$

77
DS A particle is projected from a point on a horizontal plane. How long does it take to reach its greatest height ? (Take g as $9 \cdot 8 \text{ ms}^{-2}$.)

1 Its range is 100 m. **2** Its greatest height is 30 m.

78
DS

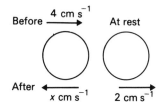

What is the ratio of the masses of the spheres in this direct impact ?

1 $x = 1$ **2** $e = 0 \cdot 75$

79
DS A body is moving in a straight line. What is its speed at time $t = 3$ seconds ?

1 After t seconds its displacement from a fixed point in the line is $(t^3 + 2t^2)$ m.
2 After t seconds its acceleration is $(6t + 4) \text{ ms}^{-2}$.

Mathematics

Pure

PAPER 8

80 Four of the following five points are collinear. Which is the odd-man-out ?

   A $(-2, -4)$ **C** $(2, 8)$ **E** $(6, 20)$
   B $(-1, 1)$ **D** $(5, 17)$

81 In triangle PQR, $p = 8$ cm, $q = 7$ cm and $r = 3$ cm. Find angle Q.

   A $30°$ **C** $90°$ **E** None of these.
   B $60°$ **D** $120°$

82 The point P $(-2, 5)$ has position vector **p** and the point Q $(4, -1)$ has position vector **q**. The point with position vector $2\mathbf{p} - 3\mathbf{q}$ has co-ordinates

   A $(2, -3)$ **C** $(-14, 17)$ **E** $(-16, 13)$
   B $(8, 7)$ **D** $(14, -17)$

83 $y = \sin 2x \cos x$. Find $\dfrac{dy}{dx}$.

   A $-2 \cos 2x \sin x$ **D** $\sin 2x \sin x + 2 \cos 2x \cos x$
   B $-\sin 2x \sin x + \cos 2x \cos x$ **E** $\sin 2x \sin x - 2 \cos 2x \cos x$
   C $-\sin 2x \sin x + 2 \cos 2x \cos x$

84 In how many ways can 5 different presents be given to 2 people so that each receives at least one present ?

   A 10   **C** 25   **E** 32
   B 23   **D** 30

85 The coefficient of x^2 in the expansion of $(1 + 2x)^{\frac{1}{2}}$ is

A -1 **C** $-\frac{1}{4}$ **E** 3
B $-\frac{1}{2}$ **D** $\frac{3}{2}$

86 The line through $(0,2)$ perpendicular to the line $3x - 4y = 7$ is

A $3x - 4y = -8$ **C** $4x - 3y = -6$ **E** $4x + 3y = 6$
B $3x + 4y = 8$ **D** $4x + 3y = 2$

87 If $\displaystyle\int_{0}^{36} \frac{dx}{2x + 9} = \ln k$ then k is

A 3 **C** $6\sqrt{2}$ **E** 81
B $4\frac{1}{2}$ **D** 9

88 If $p > q$ and $pq \neq 0$, when is it true that $\dfrac{1}{p} < \dfrac{1}{q}$?

A Always.
B Never.
C Only when $p > 0$ and $q > 0$.
D For all p, q except when both are negative.
E Whenever $pq > 0$.

89 Four cards are drawn at random from a complete pack. Which of the following gives the probability that they are the four aces ?

A $\dfrac{1}{52.51.50.49}$ **C** $\dfrac{4}{52}$ **E** $\left(\dfrac{1}{52}\right)^4$

B $\dfrac{1.2.3.4.}{52.51.50.49}$ **D** $\dfrac{4!}{52!}$

PAPER 9

90
MC
The points $(5, 1)$, $(-2, -6)$, $(-1, -7)$, $(6, 0)$ form a quadrilateral with its

  1 opposite sides equal
  2 opposite sides parallel
  3 adjacent sides perpendicular

91
MC
w is the conjugate complex of z. wz is equal to

  1 $|w|^2$ **2** $|z|^2$ **3** zw

92
MC
Which of the following lines touch the circle
$x^2 + y^2 - 6x - 2y + 9 = 0$?

  1 $4y = 3x$ **2** $y = 0$ **3** $x = 0$

93
RA
S is a fixed point and L a fixed line not passing through S.

  1 The locus of P is the parabola with focus S and directrix L.
  2 P is the centre of a circle passing through S and touching L.

94
RA
  1 $4 \sec \alpha = 5$ **2** $4 \tan \alpha = 3$

95
RA
  1 The tangents from P to the circle $x^2 + y^2 = a^2$ are perpendicular.
  2 P lies on the circle $x^2 + y^2 = 4a^2$.

96
DN
Does $y = ke^x$ satisfy the equation $p\dfrac{d^2y}{dx^2} + q\dfrac{dy}{dx} + ry = ke^x$?

  1 $k = -2$ **2** $p = 3$ **3** $q = -4$ **4** $r = 2$

97
DN
Show that $x^2 - 7x + 12$ is a factor of
$(x^2 + ax + b)(x^2 + bx + c)(x^2 + cx + d)(x^2 + dx + a)$.

  1 $a = -4$ **2** $b = 3$ **3** $c = 2$ **4** $d = -3$

98
DS
x and y are positive. Is $x + y < 1 + xy$?

  1 $x < 1$ **2** $y < x$

99
DS
Does $a \cos \theta + b = 0$ have a solution for θ in the second quadrant ?

  1 $a > b$ **2** $a > 0$

PAPER 10

100 Find the value of the term independent of x in the expansion of

$$\left(2x + \frac{3}{x^2}\right)^6.$$

A 90   **C** 720   **E** 4320

B 270   **D** 2160

101 The graph of $y = \sin x$ is the mirror image of the graph of $y = \cos x$ in the line $x = \theta$, where $0 \leqslant \theta \leqslant \pi$, and θ is

A 0   **C** $\frac{\pi}{2}$ **E** π

B $\frac{\pi}{4}$ **D** $\frac{3\pi}{4}$

102 If R is the point $(2, 5)$ and S is the point $(11, -1)$, then the point dividing RS in the ratio $1 : 2$ is

A $(5, 3)$ **C** $(8, 1)$ **E** $(24, 3)$

B $(6\frac{1}{2}, 2)$ **D** $(15, 9)$

103 If $2\cos\theta - \sin\theta$ is expressed in the form $r\cos(\theta + \alpha)$, where $r > 0$, the values of r and $\sin\alpha$ are respectively

A $5, \frac{1}{\sqrt{5}}$ **C** $\frac{1}{\sqrt{5}}, \frac{2}{\sqrt{5}}$ **E** $\sqrt{5}, \frac{2}{\sqrt{5}}$

B $\frac{1}{\sqrt{5}}, \frac{1}{\sqrt{5}}$ **D** $\sqrt{5}, \frac{1}{\sqrt{5}}$

104

The number of points of inflexion on this curve is

A 2   **C** 4   **E** 6

B 3   **D** 5

105 The sum of the reciprocals of the roots of the equation

$$3x^2 - 2x - 4 = 0 \text{ is}$$

   A $-1\frac{1}{2}$ **C** $-\frac{1}{2}$ **E** $1\frac{1}{2}$

   B $-\frac{3}{4}$ **D** $\frac{1}{2}$

106 p, q, r, s are consecutive integers in descending order.
If $pq - rs = p + q + r + s$ then s can take

   A   all values   **D**   only one value

   B   all values other than negative ones   **E**   no values at all

   C   just two values

107 How many even 4 digit numbers can be formed by using some or all of the digits 1, 2, 3, 4 allowing repetition ?

   A   12   **C**   16   **E**   256

   B   14   **D**   128

108 The complex number $4 - 3i$ has modulus

   A   1   **C**   5   **E**   25

   B   4   **D**   7

109 On the island of St. Swithun the probability that the wind will reach gale force on any day is $0 \cdot 60$ and the probability that the temperature will fall below freezing point is $0 \cdot 50$. The probability that neither of these events will occur is $0 \cdot 35$. What is the probability that both will occur ?

   A $0 \cdot 30$ **C** $0 \cdot 45$ **E** $0 \cdot 75$

   B $0 \cdot 35$ **D** $0 \cdot 65$

PAPER 11

110 If $xy = 100$ there will be a linear relationship between

MC

   1   the reciprocal of x and the reciprocal of y

   2 e^x and e^y

   3 $\ln x$ and $\ln y$

111 A cube has

MC

1 4 axes of 90° rotational symmetry

2 4 axes of 120° rotational symmetry

3 6 axes of 180° rotational symmetry (not including those of 90°)

112 If $f(x) \equiv \dfrac{1+x}{1-x}$ for $x(x^2 - 1) \neq 0$,

MC

1 $f[f(x)] \equiv -\dfrac{1}{x}$

2 $f(x).f(-x) \equiv 0$

3 $f(1/x) \equiv f(x)$

113 a and b are real.

RA

1 $a^2 + b^2 = 0$ **2** $a^3 + b^3 = 0$

114 Two circles both pass through the points (2,0) and (1,1).

RA

1 They both touch the y-axis.

2 The both touch the line $y + 1 = 0$.

115 **1** $\mathbf{u} = \cos\alpha\,\mathbf{i} + \sin\alpha\,\mathbf{j}$ for some value of α.

RA **2** $\mathbf{u}$ is a unit vector in the plane of $\mathbf{i}$ and $\mathbf{j}$.

116 The region S is bounded by the curve $y = f(x)$ and the lines $y = 0$, $x = a$

DN and $x = na$. Express as a multiple of π the volume formed by rotating S through 4 right-angles about the x-axis.

1 $n = 4$ **3** $f(a) = 2$

2 $a = 1$ **4** $f'(x) = 2x$

117 Are the points where the lines

DN

$$x + ay + b = 0$$
$$cx + dy + 1 = 0$$

meet the co-ordinate axes concyclic ?

1 $a = 2$ **3** $c = 8$

2 $b = 3$ **4** $d = 4$

118 Find the area of the triangle with vertices at the points with Cartesian

DS co-ordinates $(0, a - b)$, $(b + 1, a)$ and $(b, a + b)$.

1 $a = 5$ **2** $b = 7$

119 In which quadrant does θ lie ?

DS

1 $\sin 2\theta$ is negative   **2** $\cos 2\theta$ is positive.

PAPER 12

120 When the reflection of the point $(1, -4)$ in the origin is reflected in the line $y = x$, the resulting point is

   A $(-1,4)$ **C** $(1,4)$ **E** $(-1,-4)$
   B $(-4,1)$ **D** $(4,-1)$

121 The coefficient of x^3 in the expansion of $(1 - 2x)^{-3/2}$ is

   A $-2\frac{3}{16}$ **B** $-\frac{1}{2}$ **C** $4\frac{3}{8}$ **D** $17\frac{1}{2}$ **E** 105

122 The circle $x^2 + y^2 + 3x - 5y - 1 = 0$ has radius

   A $\sqrt{7 \cdot 5}$ **C** $\sqrt{35}$ **E** 35
   B $\sqrt{9 \cdot 5}$ **D** $9 \cdot 5$

123 $y = \dfrac{\sin x}{x}$.   Find $\dfrac{dy}{dx}$.

   A $\cos x$ **D** $\dfrac{\sin x - x \cos x}{x^2}$

   B $\dfrac{x \cos x + \sin x}{x^2}$ **E** $\dfrac{x \cos x - \sin x}{\sin^2 x}$

   C $\dfrac{x \cos x - \sin x}{x^2}$

124 The arithmetic mean of two numbers is 8 and their geometric mean is 4. The numbers are the roots of

   A $x^2 - 8x + 4 = 0$ **D** $x^2 - 16x + 2 = 0$
   B $x^2 - 16x + 4 = 0$ **E** $x^2 - 16x + 16 = 0$
   C $x^2 - 8x + 16 = 0$

125 The second derivative of $\exp(-x^2)$ with respect to x is

   A $\exp(-x^2)$ **D** $-2(2x^2 + 1)\ \exp(-x^2)$
   B $-2x\ \exp(-x^2)$ **E** $2(2x^2 - 1)\ \exp(-x^2)$
   C $4x^2\ \exp(-x^2)$

126 If $\tan \theta = \frac{1}{3}$, then $\tan 2\theta =$

   A $\frac{3}{5}$ **C** $\frac{3}{4}$ **E** $\frac{4}{3}$
   B $\frac{2}{3}$ **D** $\frac{4}{5}$

127 What is the probability that an integer chosen at random is not divisible by either 5 or 7 ?

A $\frac{12}{35}$ **C** $\frac{22}{35}$ **E** $\frac{24}{35}$

B $\frac{11}{35}$ **D** $\frac{23}{35}$

128 The number of pairs of integer values of x, y which satisfy

$$x + y \leqslant 5, \qquad x > 0 \qquad y > 0$$

simultaneously, is

A 6   **B** 9   **C** 10   **D** 12   **E** 21

129 The position vectors of P, Q are $10\mathbf{i} - 10\mathbf{j}$ and $2\mathbf{i} + 2\mathbf{j}$ respectively. What is the position vector of the point dividing PQ in the ratio $3 : -1$?

A $15\mathbf{i} - 16\mathbf{j}$ **C** $-\mathbf{i} + 4\mathbf{j}$ **E** None of these

B $7\mathbf{i} - 8\mathbf{j}$ **D** $-2\mathbf{i} + 8\mathbf{j}$

PAPER 13

130 Which of the following are polar equations of circles ?
MC

1 $r = a$ **2** $r = a \cos \theta$ **3** $r = a + a \cos \theta$

131 If $z = \cos \theta + i \sin \theta$, which of the following expressions are real ?
MC

1 $z + z^{-1}$ **2** $z - \bar{z}$ **3** $z + \bar{z}^{-1}$

132 Defining $\triangle[f(n)]$ to be $f(n + 1) - f(n)$, then
MC

1 $\triangle(\sin 2n \, \theta) = 2 \sin(2n + 1) \, \theta \cos \theta$

2 $\triangle(n^2) \equiv 2n$

3 $\triangle(\ln n) \equiv \ln(1 + n^{-1})$

133
RA $w = \dfrac{1 - z}{1 + z}$

1 $|z| = 1$ **2** $\text{Re}(w) = 0$

134
RA **1** $t = \tan \frac{\theta}{2}$

2 $\dfrac{2t}{1+t^2} = \sin \theta$

135 L is the line $2x - y + c = 0$. P is the parabola $y^2 = 4ax$.
RA
1 L touches P. **2** $a = c$

136 What are the co-ordinates of the vertex S of the parallelogram PQRS ?
DN
1 The equation of PR is $y = x$.
2 Q lies on the y-axis.
3 The gradient of PQ is $\frac{1}{2}$
4 The equation of QR is $y = 3x - 2$.

137 $f(x)$ is a decreasing function. Is $\int_{1}^{4} f(x)dx > 11$?
DN
1 $f(1) = 10$ **3** $f(3) = 4$
2 $f(2) = 6$ **4** $f(4) = 2$

138 What is the numerical value of the gradient of the chord of the
DS parabola $x = at^2$, $y = 2at$ joining the points with parameters p, q ?

1 $p + q = 5$ **2** $p - q = 2$

139 Does the line $y = mx + c$ lie entirely outside the second quadrant ?
DS **1** $m < 0$ **2** $c > 0$

PAPER 14

140 If $f(x) \equiv e^{2x}$ then $[f(x)]^2 \equiv f(y)$ where y is

A $2x$ C x^2 E $4x^2$
B $4x$ D $2x^2$

141
Find the limit as $\theta \to 0$ of $\dfrac{1 - \cos\theta}{2\sin^2\theta}$

A 0 C 1/4 E infinite
B 1/8 D 1

142 Four of the following five points are concyclic, lying on a circle with centre $(2, -1)$. Which is the odd-man-out?

A $(1,6)$ **C** $(-5, 4)$ **E** $(-3, 4)$
B $(7, -6)$ **D** $(9, -2)$

143 Expressed in prime factors the integer n is $3^p.5^q.7^r$. How many different positive integers, apart from n and unity, will divide exactly into n?

A $\dfrac{(p+q+r)!}{p!\,q!\,r!} - 2$ **D** $(p+1)(q+1)(r+1) - 2$

B $pqr - 2$ **E** $p+q+r-2$
C $p+q+r+1$

144 $p > q > 0$ and $p + q = 1$.
Which is the largest of $p^{-1}, q^{-1}, p, pq, (pq)^{-1}$?

A p^{-1} **C** p **E** $(pq)^{-1}$
B q^{-1} **D** pq

145 If $3x^2 - 4xy + 2y^2 + y + 1 = 0$, $\dfrac{dy}{dx}$ is

A $\dfrac{6x - 4y}{4x - 4y - 1}$ **C** $\dfrac{6x - 4y + 1}{4x - 4y - 1}$ **E** $\dfrac{4y - 6x}{4y + 1}$

B $\dfrac{6x}{4x - 4y - 1}$ **D** $\dfrac{6x}{4x - 1}$

146 If $z = \ln y$, δz is approximately equal to

A $\ln(y + \delta y)$ **C** $\dfrac{1}{\delta y}$ **E** $\dfrac{1}{y}$

B $\ln(\delta y)$ **D** $\dfrac{\delta y}{y}$

147 In an Argand diagram O is the origin, P the point $(2, 1)$ and Q the point $(1, 2)$. If OP represents the complex number z then OQ represents

A $\bar{z}$ **C** $-\bar{z}$ **E** $2\bar{z}$
B $i\bar{z}$ **D** $-i\bar{z}$

148 Which line, if any, is the first to contain an error ?

$$I = \int_0^{\frac{\pi}{2}} \frac{\cos\theta \; d\theta}{\cos\theta + \sin\theta}$$ line 0

By putting $\theta = \frac{\pi}{2} - \phi$,
$$I = \int_0^{\frac{\pi}{2}} \frac{\sin\phi \; d\phi}{\sin\phi + \cos\phi}$$ line 1

$$= \int_0^{\frac{\pi}{2}} \frac{\sin\theta \; d\theta}{\sin\theta + \cos\theta}$$ line 2

Adding line 0 and line 2,
$$2I = \int_0^{\frac{\pi}{2}} \frac{\cos\theta + \sin\theta \; d\theta}{\sin\theta \quad + \cos\theta}$$ line 3

Thus $I = \frac{\pi}{4}$ line 4

A line 1 **C** line 3 **E** There is no error.
B line 2 **D** line 4

149 What is the probability that tossing 4 coins simultaneously will result in 3 heads and a tail ?

A $\frac{3}{10}$ **C** $\frac{1}{5}$ **E** $\frac{1}{16}$
B $\frac{1}{4}$ **D** $\frac{1}{6}$

PAPER 15

150 If $f(x) = \exp(\sin x)$ then
MC
1 $f(0) = 1$ **2** $f'(0) = 1$ **3** $f''(0) = 1$

151 Integration by parts would be a suitable method to use in finding the
MC integral with respect to x of

1 $x \sin x$ **2** $\ln 3x$ **3** e^{4x}

152 P points are taken on the circumference of a circle and all of the chords
MC joining them in pairs are drawn. R is the maximum number of non-overlapping regions into which these lines divide the circle.

1 If $P = 4$, $R = 8$. **2** If $P = 5$, $R = 16$. **3** If $P = 6$, $R = 32$.

153 1 $\operatorname{Im}(z_1 + z_2) = 0$
RA 2 $z_1 = \bar{z}_2$

154 **1** $\sin \alpha + \cos \alpha = 0$ **2** $\sin 2\alpha = -1$
RA

155 The equations of two circles are
RA $(x - 5)^2 + (y - 12)^2 = r^2$ and $x^2 + y^2 = 81$.

   1 $r = 4$ **2** The circles touch each other.

156 Is $\dfrac{2ax - c^2}{(x - c)(x - d)} = \dfrac{a + b}{x - c} + \dfrac{a - b}{x - d}$
DN

   true for all values of x other than c and d ?

   1 $a = 1$ **3** $c = -1$
   2 $b = \frac{1}{2}$ **4** $d = 1$

157 Find the area of the triangle formed by the pole and the points with
DN polar co-ordinates (r_1, θ_1) and (r_2, θ_2).

   1 $r_1 = r_2 + 2$ **3** $r_2 = 2$
   2 $\theta_1 = \theta_2 + \dfrac{\pi}{3}$ **4** $\theta_2 = \dfrac{\pi}{3}$

158 In an Argand diagram do the points which represent the complex
DS numbers p, q, r lie at the vertices of a right-angled triangle ?

   1 $|p - r|^2 = |r - q|^2 + |q - p|^2$
   2 $\arg \dfrac{q - r}{q - p} = \dfrac{\pi}{2}$

159 Does the equation $4 \cos \theta + 3 \sin \theta = k$ have a solution for θ in the first
DS quadrant ?

   1 It has a solution in the third quadrant.
   2 It has a solution in the fourth quadrant.

PAPER 16

160 The substitution $t = \tan \dfrac{\theta}{2}$ transforms the equation
        $3 \sin \theta - 4 \cos \theta = 2$ into

   A $5t^2 + 8t - 1 = 0$ **D** $t^2 + 2t - 2 = 0$
   B $2t^2 + 3t - 3 = 0$ **E** $t^2 + 3t - 3 = 0$
   C $t^2 - t + 1 = 0$

161 Use the binomial expansion to obtain a three term approximation for $(x^6 + 3x^5)^{1/3}$ when x is large.

A $x^2 + x - 2$
B $x^2 + x - 1$
C $x^2 + x - \frac{1}{3}$
D $x^2 + x + 2$
E None of these, for the binomial series may not be used when x is large.

162 The gradient of the line joining the focus of the parabola $y^2 = 4ax$ to the point $(at^2, 2at)$ is

A $\dfrac{2t}{1 + t^2}$ C $\dfrac{2t}{1 - t^2}$ E $\dfrac{t^2 + 1}{2t}$

B $\dfrac{2t}{t^2 - 1}$ D $\dfrac{t^2 + 1}{2t}$

163 The functions being real, solve completely the equation

$$\log_2 8x + \log_2 2x = 6.$$

A $1 \cdot 5$ C 2 E $6 \cdot 4$
B $1 \cdot 5$ and $-1 \cdot 5$ D 2 and -2

164 If $y = 3x^2 - 0 \cdot 01$ and $\delta x = 0 \cdot 1$, then the exact value of δy when $x = 1$ is

A $0 \cdot 57$ C $0 \cdot 61$ E $0 \cdot 63$
B $0 \cdot 60$ D $0 \cdot 62$

165

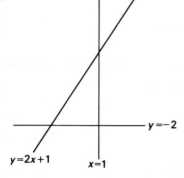

$y = -2$

$y = 2x + 1$ $x = 1$

The lines whose equations are given in the diagram divide the plane into seven regions. The number of regions in which points satisfy
$(x - 1)(y + 2)(y - 2x - 1) > 0$
is

A 1   C 3   E 5
B 2   D 4

166 A piece of string is cut in two at a point selected at random. What is the probability that one piece is at least five times as long as the other ?

A $\frac{1}{6}$ **B** $\frac{1}{5}$ **C** $\frac{1}{3}$ **D** $\frac{2}{5}$ **E** $\frac{1}{2}$

167 A geometric series has first term 1 and common ratio $\frac{1}{2}$. The difference between the sum to infinity and the sum of the first k terms can be expressed as

A 2^{1-k} **C** 2^k **E** none of these

B 2^{k-1} **D** 2^{-k}

168 Which one of the following five expressions is not identical to any of the others ?

A $\cos^4\theta - \sin^4\theta$ **C** $\cos 2\theta$ **E** $1 - \cos\theta$

B $1 + \cos\theta$ **D** $2\cos^2(\theta/2)$

169 $\sqrt{5 + 2\sqrt{6}} - \sqrt{5 - 2\sqrt{6}}$ is equal to

A $2\sqrt{2}$ **C** $2\sqrt{2\sqrt{6}}$ **E** none of these

B $\sqrt{10}$ **D** 8

PAPER 17

170 The locus of the point given parametrically by

MC

$$x = \frac{t^2 - 1}{t^2 + 1}, y = 2t$$

will meet

1 any line parallel to the x-axis in 1 real point

2 any line parallel to the y-axis in 2 real points, possibly coincident

3 any oblique line in at most 2 real points

171
MC In which of the following differential equations are the variables separable ?

1 $\dfrac{dy}{dx} = x - y$

2 $\dfrac{dy}{dx} = \ln(x - y)$

3 $\dfrac{dy}{dx} = \exp(x - y)$

172
MC If $f(x) \in Q$, the set of all functions of the form $ax^2 + bx + c$ with $a \neq 0$, and $g(x) \in L$, the set of all functions of the form $px + q$ with $p \neq 0$, then

1 $[f(x + 1) - f(x)] \in L$
2 $f'(x) \in L$
3 $\int_0^x g(t)\, dt \in Q$

173
RA $f(x) \equiv ax^2 + bx + c \quad (a > 0)$

1 $f(x) < 0$ for some values of x **2** $b^2 < 4ac$

174
RA $p, q, r,$ are positive.

1 $p^2 + q^2 - r^2 = 0$ **2** $p + q - r = 0$

175
RA **1** $2^n = n^2$ **2** $\displaystyle\sum_1^n 2^r = \sum_1^n r^2$

176
DN In $\triangle PQR$, find $\angle Q$.

1 $p = 7$ cm   **3** $\angle P = 60°$
2 $q = 8$ cm   **4** The triangle has area $10\sqrt{3}$ cm^2.

177
DN How many tangents to the parabola $y^2 = 4ax$ pass through the point (h, k) ?

1 $a > 4$ **3** $k > -10$
2 $h > 9$ **4** $k < 12$

178
DS Is the triangle with sides a, b, c obtuse angled ?

1 $a^2 + b^2 < c^2$ **2** $a^2 < b^2 + c^2$

179 $f(x) \equiv x^3 - ax + b$
DS

Given that a and b are real, what are their values ?

1 $f(-4) = 0$ **2** $f(2 + i) = 0$

PAPER 18

180 When simplified the modulus of $1 + \cos 2\theta + i \sin 2\theta$ is

  A $4\cos^2 \theta$ **D** $2 \sin \theta$

  B $4\sin^2 \theta$ **E** not necessarily any of these

  C $2 \cos \theta$

181 12 people are to be divided into 3 groups, the first to contain 5 people, the second 4 and the last 3. Which of the following expressions gives the number of ways in which this can be done ?

  A $^{12}C_5 \times {}^7C_4$ **C** $^{12}C_5 + {}^7C_4 + 1$ **E** $^{12}P_5 + {}^7P_4$

  B $^{12}C_5 + {}^7C_4$ **D** $^{12}P_5 \times {}^7P_4$

182 What is the derivative of a^x with respect to x ?

  A a^x **C** $a^{x \log_e a}$ **E** $a^x \log_a e$

  B xa^{x-1} **D** $a^x \log_e a$

183 In which of the regions P, Q, R, S is the inequality
$(x^2 + y^2 - 4)(y - 1) < 0$ satisfied ?

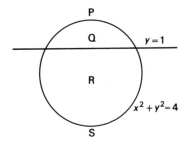

  A Q only   **C** S only   **E** P and R

  B R only   **D** Q and S

184 Which of the following sketch graphs is that of the function xe^{-x} ?

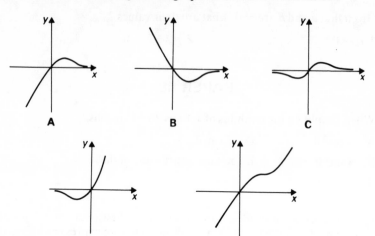

185 Express $\sin \theta$ in terms of c where $c = \cot \frac{1}{2}\theta$

A $\dfrac{2c}{1+c^2}$ C $\dfrac{c^2-1}{c^2+1}$ E   None of these.

B $\dfrac{2c}{c^2-1}$ D $\dfrac{1+c^2}{2c}$

186 A point has polar co-ordinates $r = 2$, $\theta = \dfrac{4\pi}{3}$. What are its Cartesian co-ordinates referred to the same origin and with the initial line as the x-axis ?

A $(1, -\sqrt{3})$ C $(-1, \sqrt{3})$ E $(-1, -\sqrt{3})$
B $(-\sqrt{3}, 1)$ D $(-\sqrt{3}, -1)$

187

PQR is a straight line. $QR = 2PQ$.
Express **r** in terms of **p** and **q**.

A $2\mathbf{p} + 3\mathbf{q}$ C $2\mathbf{p} - 3\mathbf{q}$ E $-2\mathbf{p} + 3\mathbf{q}$
B $-10\mathbf{p} + 15\mathbf{q}$ D $10\mathbf{p} - 15\mathbf{q}$

38

188 What is the probability that a three digit car number contains at least one 5 ?

A $\frac{271}{1000}$ C $\frac{14}{45}$ E $\frac{19}{50}$

B $\frac{7}{25}$ D $\frac{1}{3}$

189 Of the integrals

$$\int_0^\pi \sin^3 \theta \cos^3 \theta \, d\theta, \qquad \int_0^2 t^3(4-t^2)^2 dt, \qquad \int_0^\pi x^2 \cos x \, dx$$

one is negative, one is positive and one is zero. Without evaluating them determine which is which.

A − 0 +   C + 0 −   E 0 + −
B + − 0   D 0 − +

PAPER 19

190
MC A particular solution of the differential equation

$$\frac{dy}{dx} = e^{x-y}$$

is given by

1 $y = x$ 2 $y = \ln(1 + e^x)$ 3 $y = \ln(2e^x)$

191 For which of the following integrals is it appropriate to make the
MC substitution $x = a \sin \theta$?

1 $\int \frac{dx}{\sqrt{(a^2 + x^2)}}$ 2 $\int \frac{dx}{\sqrt{(x^2 - a^2)}}$ 3 $\int \frac{dx}{\sqrt{(a^2 - x^2)}}$

192 The cardioid $r = a(1 + \cos \theta)$ has
MC

1 precisely two tangents in any given direction
2 a tangent which is also a normal to the curve
3 a tangent which touches the curve at two distinct points

193
RA
H is the point (1,0), K the point (– 1,0), and P is a variable point.

1 PH – PK = 2

2 The locus of P is the x-axis.

194
RA
a, b, c are real.

1 $a^2 + b^2 + c^2 = bc + ca + ab$

2 $a = b = c$

195
RA
1 $\mathbf{r}$ can be expressed in the form $\cos\theta\mathbf{i} + \sin\theta\mathbf{j}$.

2 $\dfrac{d\mathbf{r}}{d\theta}$ is a vector perpendicular to $\mathbf{r}$.

196
DN
The point P in an Argand diagram represents the product of the complex numbers $r_1(\cos\theta_1 + i\sin\theta_1)$, $r_2(\cos\theta_2 + i\sin\theta_2)$. What are the numerical values of the Cartesian co-ordinates of P ?

1 $r_1 - r_2 = 0$

2 $r_1 + r_2 = 4$

3 $\theta_1 + \theta_2 = \dfrac{3\pi}{4}$

4 $\theta_1 - \theta_2 = \dfrac{\pi}{4}$

197
DN
X, Y, Z are three events. What is the value of $P(Y \cap Z)$?

1 $P(X \mid Y) = \frac{1}{6}$

2 $P(Z) = \frac{1}{2}$

3 $P(X \cap Y) = \frac{1}{10}$

4 $P(Z \mid Y) = \frac{1}{3}$

198
DS
P and Q are the points, other than the origin, common to the curve $y = x^3 + ax^2 + bx$ and the line $y = mx$. Find the numerical value of the abscissa of the mid-point of PQ.

1 $m = 4$

2 $a = -3$

199
DS
Find numerically the mean value of $\pi \sin ax$ in the range $\dfrac{k\pi}{a} \leqslant x \leqslant \dfrac{(k+1)\pi}{a}$

1 k is even.

2 $a = 3$

PAPER 20

200 Find the gradient of the line given parametrically by

$$x = 6 - 5t$$
$$y = 5 + 6t.$$

A $\dfrac{5}{6}$ **C** $\dfrac{6}{5}$ **E** $\dfrac{5 + 6t}{6 - 5t}$

B $-\dfrac{5}{6}$ **D** $-\dfrac{6}{5}$

201 The number of values of y, real or complex, which satisfy the simultaneous equations

$$x = y - \frac{1}{y}$$
$$y = x + \frac{1}{x}$$

is

A 0   **B** 2   **C** 3   **D** 4   **E** infinite

202 $\dfrac{\mathrm{d}}{\mathrm{d}\theta} \sec^3 \theta$ is

A $3 \sec^3 \theta \tan \theta$ **C** $3 \sec^2 \theta \tan^2 \theta$ **E** $3 \sec \theta \tan^2 \theta$
B $3 \sec^2 \theta$ **D** $3 \sec^2 \theta \tan^2 \theta$

203 If $\int \sin^2 4x \cos 4x \, \mathrm{d}x = k \sin^3 4x + c$ then k is

A $\frac{1}{12}$ **C** $\frac{1}{3}$ **E** $-\frac{1}{3}$
B $\frac{1}{4}$ **D** $-\frac{1}{4}$

204 A curve is given parametrically by the equations

$$x = \sec\theta, \quad y = 1 + \tan\theta.$$

The equation of the curve is $x^2 =$

A y^2 **C** $y^2 - 2y$ **E** $y^2 - 2y + 2$
B $y^2 - 2$ **D** $2y - y^2$

205 The graph of $|x| - |y| = 1$ is of the form

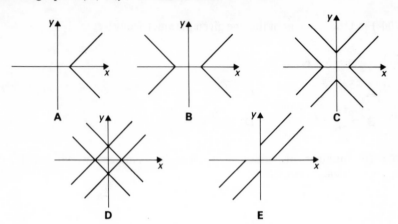

206 S_n denotes the sum of n terms of a G.P. with first term $0 \cdot 9$ and common ratio $0 \cdot 1$. As $n \to \infty$, $S_n \to S$. The smallest value of n for which $S - S_n < 10^{-5}$ is

A less than 4   **B** 4   **C** 5   **D** 6   **E** more than 6

207 In a plane there are two sets of parallel lines, the m lines of one set being perpendicular to the n lines of the other. How many rectangles (possibly including squares) do these lines form ?

A mn **B** $(m-1)(n-1)$ **C** $mn(m-1)(n-1)$
D $\frac{1}{4}mn(m-1)(n-1)$ **E** $\frac{1}{2}m(m-1) + \frac{1}{2}n(n-1)$

208 As $x \to 0$, the limit of $\dfrac{\sin x^\circ}{x}$ is

A 0   **C** 1   **E** none of these

B $\dfrac{\pi}{180}$ **D** $\dfrac{180}{\pi}$

209 The product of the complex numbers $\dfrac{1-i}{\sqrt{2}}$ and $\dfrac{\sqrt{3}+i}{2}$ has argument

A $\dfrac{-5\pi}{12}$ C $\dfrac{\pi}{12}$ E   none of these

B $\dfrac{-\pi}{12}$ D $\dfrac{5\pi}{12}$

PAPER 21

210
MC In which of the following differential equations are the variables separable ?

1 $x + y\,\dfrac{dy}{dx} = x\,\sin^2 y$

2 $x + y\,\dfrac{dy}{dx} = y\,\sin^2 x$

3 $x + y\,\dfrac{dy}{dx} = \sin^2 y$

211
MC An approximate value for $\ln 3$ is to be found by using the first few terms of a series. It can be obtained by substituting

1 $x = 2$ in the series for $\ln(1 + x)$

2 $x = \frac{4}{5}$ in the series for $\frac{1}{2}\ln\dfrac{(1+x)}{(1-x)}$

3 $x = -\frac{1}{2}$ in the series for $\frac{1}{2}\ln\dfrac{(1+x)}{(1-x)}$

212
MC

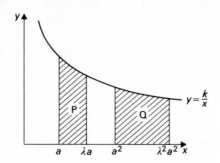

The expression for $\dfrac{\text{area } P}{\text{area } Q}$ is independent of

1 k **2** a **3** λ

213 **1** $\sin(\dfrac{\pi}{2} + \alpha) = \cos(\dfrac{\pi}{2} - \alpha)$
RA
        2 $\sin(\dfrac{\pi}{3} + \alpha) = \cos(\dfrac{\pi}{3} - \alpha)$

214 $p(x)$ is a polynomial.
RA
        1 The number of distinct points in which the graph of $y = p(x)$ meets the x-axis is three.

        2 The number of asymptotes in the graph of $y = \dfrac{1}{p(x)}$ is three.

215 **1** P is a point on the parabola $y^2 = 2(1 - x)$.
RA **2** P has parametric co-ordinates $x = \cos 2t, y = 2 \sin t$.

216 Does $a^p + b^q = 0 \;\Rightarrow\; a^q + b^r = 0$?
DN
        1 a and b are real.   **3** q is even.
        2 p is even.   **4** r is even.

217 (h, k) is the mid-point of the chord $bx + cy + d = 0$ of the parabola
DN $y^2 = 4ax$. Find the numerical value of k.

        1 $a = 2$ **3** $c = -1$
        2 $b = 3$ **4** $d = -4$

218 m and n are positive integers. Arrange
DS
$$\frac{m}{n}, \quad \frac{n}{m}, \quad \frac{m^2}{n^2}, \quad \frac{n^2}{m^2}$$

in ascending order of magnitude.

1 $\dfrac{m}{n} > \dfrac{n}{m}$ **2** $\dfrac{n}{m} > \dfrac{n^2}{m^2}$

219 The tangent at $x = t$ to the curve $y = e^{kx}$ meets the x-axis at T. If N is the
DS point $(t,0)$, find the numerical value of the length TN.

1 $k = 2$ **2** $t = 3$

PAPER 22

220 How many points common to the half line $\theta = \dfrac{3\pi}{4}$ and the spiral $r = \dfrac{\theta}{5\pi}$
lie inside the circle $r = 1$?

A 1 **C** 3 **E** More than 4
B 2 **D** 4

221 If the ' distance ' between two points (x_1, y_1), (x_2, y_2) in the Cartesian
plane is defined to be

$$|x_1 - x_2| + |y_1 - y_2|$$

then the locus of points at unit ' distance ' from the origin looks like

   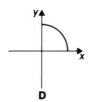

A **B** **C** **D**

E none of these

222 Find the locus of the foot of the perpendicular from the origin to the line
$y + tx = 1 + t^2$ as t varies.

A $x^2 + y^2 = y(y^2 - x^2)$ **C** $x^2 + y^2 = 1$ **E** $y = 1$
B $x^2 + y^2 = 2x^2 y$ **D** $x = t$

45

223 Find the ratio of the probabilities that two cards drawn at random from a pack are both aces, in the cases
  (i) the first card is replaced and the pack shuffled before the second is drawn
  (ii) there is no such replacement

A $8:3$ **C** $4:3$ **E** $52:51$
B $5:3$ **D** $17:13$

224 If $\dfrac{dy}{dx} = y^2 \cos x$ and $y = -1$ when $x = 0$, the value of y when $x = \dfrac{\pi}{2}$ is

A $-\frac{1}{2}$ **C** -1 **E** infinite
B $\frac{1}{2}$ **D** 1

225 The quadratic equation with roots $2 + 3i$, $2 - 3i$ is

A $x^2 + 4x + 13 = 0$ **D** $x^2 + 4x - 5 = 0$
B $x^2 - 4x + 13 = 0$ **E** $x^2 - 4x - 5 = 0$
C $x^2 + 4x - 13 = 0$

226 The function $x^3 + 3x^2 - 9x + 7$ increases with x only when

A $x > 0$ **C** $-1 < x < 3$ **E** $x < -1$ or $x > 3$
B $-3 < x < 1$ **D** $x < -3$ or $x > 1$

227 If $\int \dfrac{dx}{x^2\sqrt{(x-1)}}$ is transformed to $\int f(\theta)\,d\theta$ by means of the substitution $x = \sec^2\theta$ then $f(\theta)$ is

A $2\cos^3\theta \cot\theta$ **C** $2\cos^2\theta \sin\theta$ **E** $\cos^4\theta \cot\theta$
B $2\cos^2\theta$ **D** $2\cos^3\theta$

228 Estimate the area under the curve $y = 2^x$ between $x = 0$ and $x = 2$ by using Simpson's Rule with 3 ordinates.

A 3 **B** 4 **C** $4\frac{1}{3}$ **D** $4\frac{1}{2}$ **E** $8\frac{2}{3}$

229 When simplified, an expression for the argument of
  $1 + \cos\theta + i\sin\theta$ is

A $2\cos\dfrac{\theta}{2}$ **C** θ **E** $\dfrac{\pi}{2} - \dfrac{\theta}{2}$

B $2\sin\dfrac{\theta}{2}$ **D** $\dfrac{\theta}{2}$

PAPER 23

230
MC An approximation for $\sqrt[3]{10}$ can be obtained by using the binomial expansion of $(1+x)^{\frac{1}{3}}$ in ascending powers of x and putting x equal to

1 $\frac{1}{4}$ **2** 9 **3** $\frac{1}{9}$

231
MC $\displaystyle\int_{a}^{b} \frac{dx}{3x-2}$ can be evaluated if

1 $a=-1, b=1$ **2** $a=-1, b=-\frac{1}{2}$ **3** $a=\frac{3}{2}, b=1$

232
MC Which of the following are the equations of tangents to the circle with polar equation $r=4\cos\theta$?

1 $r\cos\theta=4$ **2** $r\sin\theta=2$ **3** $\theta=\dfrac{\pi}{2}$

233
RA X and Y are two events with $P(X)=0\cdot8$.

1 $P(Y)\geqslant0\cdot3$ **2** $P(X\cap Y)\geqslant0\cdot1$

234
RA **1** The graph of y against x is a straight line.
2 The graph of $\ln y$ against $\ln x$ is a straight line.

235
RA In an Argand diagram O is the origin and P_1, P_2 represent the non-zero complex numbers z_1, z_2 respectively.

1 Re $\dfrac{z_1}{z_2}=0$ **2** OP_1 is perpendicular to OP_2.

236
DN What is the gradient of the curve $y=f(x)$ at the point where $x=1$?
1 $f(x)$ is a cubic polynomial.
2 The curve has a turning point at the origin.
3 $f(x)$ has a minimum value when $x=-1$.
4 $f(1)=-5$

237
DN Find the area of triangle OPQ, O being the origin.

1 P lies on $x=1$. **3** Q lies on $x-y=1$.
2 P lies on $y=1$. **4** Q lies on $x+y=5$.

238
DS What is the locus of P ?
1 All points on the x-axis lie on the locus.
2 No point off the x-axis lies on the locus.

239
DS Does the line $\dfrac{x}{a}+\dfrac{y}{b}=1$ meet the parabola $y^2=4x$ in real points ?
1 $a>0$ **2** $b>0$

PAPER 24

240 Arrange the integrals

$$P = \int_0^{\pi/2} \sin^2 x \, dx$$

$$Q = \int_0^{\pi/2} \cos x \, dx$$

$$R = \int_0^{\pi/2} \sin^3 x \, dx$$

in ascending order of magnitude.

A P R Q   **C** Q P R   **E** R Q P
B R P Q   **D** Q R P

241 The line $x + 3y = 3$ meets the circle $x^2 + y^2 = 4$ at the points P and Q. Which of the following equations will, when solved for θ, give the angles which OP and OQ make with the x-axis ?

A $\cos \theta + 3\sin \theta = 3$
B $\cos \theta + 3\sin \theta = 6$
C $2\cos \theta + 6\sin \theta = 3$
D $4\cos \theta + 12\sin \theta = 3$
E $6\cos \theta + 2\sin \theta = 3$

242 The locus of M, the mid-point of the line joining the focus of the parabola $y^2 = 4ax$ to a variable point on the curve, is

A $y^2 = 2ax + a^2$ **D** $y^2 = ax - a^2$
B $y^2 + 2ax = a^2$ **E** $y^2 = 2ax$
C $y^2 = 2ax - a^2$

243 If $f(x) \equiv \dfrac{x^2 - 9}{x^2 - x - 6}$ then $f(3)$ is

A   zero   **C**   unity   **E**   1·2
B   infinite   **D**   indeterminate

244 In 1974, after England had played 500 Tests, they had won the toss 250 times. What is the probability that England will win the toss exactly 250 times in the next 500 Tests ?

A   1   **C** $(\frac{1}{2})^{500}$ **E** $^{500}C_{250} \, (\frac{1}{2})^{500}$
B $(\frac{1}{2})^{250}$ **D** $^{500}C_{250}(\frac{1}{2})^{250}$

245 Use the approximation $\cos \theta \approx 1 - \frac{1}{2}\theta^2$ to find an approximate value for $\cos 2°$ given that $\cos 4° \approx 0\cdot9976$.

  A 0·9988   **C** 0·9992   **E** 0·9996
  B 0·9990   **D** 0·9994

246 In how many different cyclic orders (counting clockwise and anti-clockwise as distinct) can 12 knights seat themselves at a round table if two of them will not sit together ?

  A 11.11!   **C** 12.9.10!   **E** 9.10!
  B 11!   **D** 10.10!

247 The solution of the inequality $(x^2 - 1)(x + 2) > 0$ is

  A $x > 1$ **C** $x > 1$ or $x < -2$ **E** $x < -2$ or $-1 < x < 1$
  B $x > -2$ **D** $-2 < x < -1$ or $x > 1$

248 If $x = t^3, y = t^2$, the value of $\dfrac{\mathrm{d}^2 y}{\mathrm{d}x^2}$ at $t = 1$ is

  A -2 **C** $-\frac{2}{9}$ **E** 2
  B $-\frac{2}{3}$ **D** $\frac{1}{3}$

249 The general solution of $2\cos \theta - 1 = 0$ is

  A $n\pi + \dfrac{\pi}{3}$ **C** $2n\pi + \dfrac{\pi}{3}$ **E** none of these

  B $n\pi + (-1)^n \dfrac{\pi}{3}$ **D** $2n\pi + (-1)^n \dfrac{\pi}{3}$

PAPER 25

**250
MC**

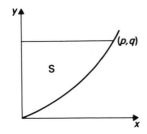

The area S is rotated through 4 right angles about the line $y = q$. The volume produced is given by

1 $\pi p q^2 - \int_0^p \pi y^2 \, \mathrm{d}x$ **2** $\int_0^q 2\pi (q - y) x \, \mathrm{d}y$ **3** $\int_0^p \pi (q - y)^2 \, \mathrm{d}x$

251
MC The circle with polar equation $r = 16 \cos \theta$
1 has radius 16
2 has the initial line as a tangent
3 passes through the pole

252
MC $f(z_1 z_2) \equiv f(z_1) f(z_2)$ if $f(z) \equiv$
1 $\bar{z}$ 2 $|z|$ 3 $\arg z$

253
RA 1 As $x \to \infty$, $f'(x) \to 0$.
2 The graph of $y = f(x)$ has an asymptote in the direction of the x-axis.

254
RA 1 $\text{Re}(\cos \theta + i \sin \theta)^n = 0$
2 $\text{Im}(\cos \theta + i \sin \theta)^n = 1$

255
RA $p(x)$ is a polynomial.
1 $y = p(x)$ has a stationary value at $x = a$.
2 $(x - a)^2$ is a factor of $p(x)$.

256
DN $p(x) \equiv ax^3 + bx^2 + cx + d$
How many roots of the equation $p(x) = 0$ are real ?

1 $p(1) < 0$ 3 $p'(0) < 0$
2 $p(0) > 0$ 4 $a > 0$

257
DN Is the binomial expansion of $\left(\dfrac{a}{x} + \dfrac{x}{b}\right)^n$, as a series in ascending powers of x, a valid one ?

1 $a = 2$ 3 $x = 3$
2 $b = 5$ 4 $n = \frac{1}{2}$

258
DS The line $x = t$ meets the x-axis at P and it meets the curve $y^2 = ax + b$ at Q. (a, b and $at + b$ are positive.) The normal to the curve at Q meets the x-axis at R. What is the numerical value of the length PR ?

1 $a = 3$ 2 $t = 1$

259
DS Find numerically the mean value of e^{ax} in the range $b \leqslant x \leqslant 2b$.
1 $a = 2$ 2 $ab = 2$

PAPER 26

260 Which is the first line to contain an error ?

$$\int \tan x \sec^2 x \, dx = \int \tan x \, d(\tan x) \qquad \textbf{A}$$

$$= \tfrac{1}{2}\tan^2 x \qquad \textbf{B}$$

$$\int \tan x \sec^2 x \, dx = \int \sec x \, d(\sec x) \qquad \textbf{C}$$

$$= \tfrac{1}{2}\sec^2 x \qquad \textbf{D}$$

$$\text{therefore } \tan x = \sec x. \qquad \textbf{E}$$

261 An approximate value of $\displaystyle\int_0^{0\cdot2} \frac{dx}{(1+x^3)^{\frac{1}{2}}}$ obtained by using the first two terms of a binomial expansion is

A $0\cdot1980$ **C** $0\cdot1998$ **E** $0\cdot2002$
B $0\cdot1996$ **D** $0\cdot2000$

262 What is the probability of scoring 6 by throwing two unbiased dice and adding together the two numbers shown ?

A $\tfrac{1}{12}$ **B** $\tfrac{5}{36}$ **C** $\tfrac{1}{6}$ **D** $\tfrac{1}{4}$ **E** $\tfrac{5}{12}$

263 If $\arctan\tfrac{1}{2} + \arctan\tfrac{1}{3} = \arctan x$ then x is

A 1 **C** $\tfrac{5}{7}$ **E** $\tfrac{1}{7}$
B $\tfrac{5}{6}$ **D** $\tfrac{1}{5}$

264 If, when θ is small, $\cos 4\theta \approx 1 + k\,\theta^2$ then k is

A -16 **C** -2 **E** 8
B -8 **D** 2

265 In an Argand diagram the points which represent the complex numbers z, $-\bar{z}$, z^{-1} and $-\bar{z}^{-1}$ necessarily lie at the vertices of a

A square   **C** parallelogram   **E** trapezium
B rectangle   **D** rhombus

266 The solution of $(4x - 3)(x + 1) > 2$ is

A $-1 < x < \tfrac{5}{4}$ **D** $x > \tfrac{5}{4}$ or $x < -1$
B $-\tfrac{5}{4} < x < 1$ **E** $x < -\tfrac{5}{4}$ or $x > 1$
C $1 < x < \tfrac{5}{4}$

267 Which one of the following five expressions is not identical to any of the others ?

A $\tan \theta + \cot \theta$ **C** 1 **E** $2 \operatorname{cosec} 2\theta$
B $\operatorname{cosec}^2 \theta - \cot^2 \theta$ **D** $\operatorname{cosec} \theta \cot \theta$

268 The coefficient of x^4 in the series for e^{-2x} is

A $-\frac{2}{3}$ **B** $\frac{1}{24}$ **C** $\frac{1}{12}$ **D** $\frac{2}{3}$ **E** 4

269 The area in the first quadrant enclosed by the lines $x = 4$, $y = 0$ and the curve given parametrically by $x = t^2$, $y = t^3$, when expressed as an integral with respect to t, is

A $\int_0^2 t^3 \, dt$ **C** $\int_0^2 2t^4 \, dt$ **E** $\int_0^2 3t^4 \, dt$

B $\int_0^4 t^3 \, dt$ **D** $\int_0^4 2t^4 \, dt$

PAPER 27

270 For the circle $x^2 + y^2 = a^2$, $\dfrac{d^2 y}{dx^2}$ is positive in
MC
1 quadrant 1 **2** quadrant 2 **3** quadrant 3

271 For two unequal positive numbers
MC
1 their A.M. is less than their G.M.
2 the square of their A.M. is greater than the A.M. of their squares
3 the square of their G.M. is equal to the G.M. of their squares

272 Between which of the following pairs of limits is $\int \sin 2x \, dx$ equal to
MC zero ?

1 $0, \pi/2$ **2** $0, \pi$ **3** $-\alpha, \alpha$

273
RA

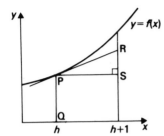

For the function sketched above

1 PQ = RS for all values of h

2 $f(x) \equiv ke^x$ for some value of k

274 $q(x)$ is a quadratic function.
RA
  1 The graph of $y = q(x)$ meets the x-axis in two distinct points.

  2 The graph of $y = \dfrac{1}{q(x)}$ has precisely two branches.

275 **1** $a^2 + b^2 > 2$
RA **2** The equation $a\sin\theta + b\cos\theta = 2$ has no solutions.

276 Find (x, y).
DN
  1 $x \geqslant 1$ **3** $x + y \leqslant 2$

  2 $y \leqslant 2$ **4** $y \geqslant x$

277 $f(x) \equiv a\, x^m + b\, n^x$ where a, b, m, n are constants.
DN Find the numerical value of $f'(0)$.

  1 $a = 5$ **3** $m = 3$

  2 $b = 4$ **4** $n = 2$

278 Does the curve $r = f(\theta)$ have an axis of symmetry ?
DS
  1 $f(\theta) \equiv f(-\theta)$ **2** $f(\theta) \equiv f(\pi - \theta)$

279 Are the numbers w and z both real ?
DS
  1 $\mathrm{Re}(wz) = \mathrm{Re}\,w \cdot \mathrm{Re}\,z$ **2** $\mathrm{Im}(wz) = \mathrm{Im}\,w \cdot \mathrm{Im}\,z$

Mathematics

Mechanics

PAPER 28

280 A block of weight W slides down a fixed slope of angle $\arctan\frac{3}{4}$. The coefficient of friction is $\frac{1}{2}$. The horizontal component of the resultant force acting on the block is

A zero   **C** $\dfrac{W}{4}$ **E** $\dfrac{2W}{5}$

B $\dfrac{6W}{25}$ **D** $\dfrac{4W}{25}$

281

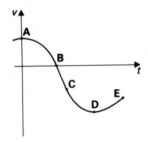

An accurate velocity-time graph of the motion of a particle is shown in the diagram. **A** and **D** are turning points and **C** is a point of inflexion. At which point of the graph is the magnitude of the acceleration greatest ?

282 Power is measured in

A joules   **C** newtons   **E** watts
B kilograms   **D** newton-seconds

283 A particle has initial velocity 3 ms⁻¹ and its acceleration t seconds later is $(6t^2 + 4t - 3)$ ms⁻². After 2 seconds, its velocity in ms⁻¹ is

A 15   **C** 21   **E** 31
B 18   **D** 27

284

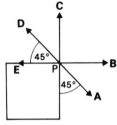

The square is a vertical section through the centre of a uniform cube standing on very rough horizontal ground. The cube is to be tilted by applying at P as small a force as possible. In which direction is this force to be applied ?

285 A stone is thrown vertically upwards. What is the form of the graph of its kinetic energy against time ?

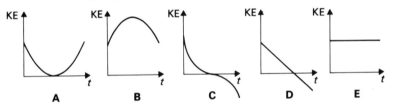

286
MC

The diagram shows a uniform rod of weight 15N resting horizontally on two supports. A vertical force is applied to an end of the rod so that the rod just ceases to bear on one of the supports. This force can be

1 3N   **2** 5N   **3** 15N

55

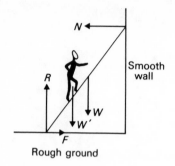

Smooth
wall

Rough ground

As the man slowly ascends the ladder, which does not slip, which of the following forces increase ?

1 R **2** F **3** N

288
MC

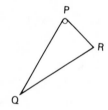

The diagram shows a uniform rod QR supported by a light string tied to its ends and passing over a smooth peg P. In equilibrium it is necessary that

1 the mid-point of the rod is vertically below P
2 PQ and PR are equally inclined to the horizontal
3 QR is horizontal

289
MC

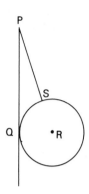

The diagram shows a uniform sphere, centre R, resting against a smooth vertical wall PQ, and supported by a string PS.

1 $\angle$ PSR = 180°   **2** $\angle$ PQR = 90°
3 $\triangle$PQR will serve as triangle of forces for the 3 forces acting on the sphere.

PAPER 29

290 A particle is moving along the x-axis.
RA
   1 The square of the velocity of the particle is proportional to x.
   2 The acceleration of the particle is constant.

291 Two bodies collide directly.
RA
   1 The bodies coalesce.   **2** No kinetic energy is lost.

292 A particle is in contact with an inclined plane of angle α and the
RA coefficient of friction between it and the plane is μ.

   1 The particle is at rest.   **2** $\mu = \tan \alpha$

293 A car accelerates along a straight horizontal road with its engine
DN exerting a constant tractive force ; the resistance to motion is negligible.
What is the numerical value of the speed after 10 seconds ?

   1 The tractive force is 300 N.   **3** Its initial speed is zero.
   2 The mass of the car is 1000 kg. **4** The value of g is $9\cdot8\,\mathrm{ms^{-2}}$.

294
DN
A car of mass M travels with constant speed v in a horizontal circle of radius r round a circular racetrack banked at an angle θ to the horizontal. What is the numerical value of the resultant force acting on the car ?

1 $M = 1$ tonne

2 $v = 25$ ms^{-1}

3 $r = 200$ m

4 $\theta = 10°$

295
DN
A piledriver of mass M falls through a height h on to a pile and does not rebound after impact. What is the resistance of the ground, assuming it to be uniform ? Take $g = 10$ ms^{-2}.

1 $M = 1 \cdot 5$ tonne

2 The mass of the pile is $\dfrac{M}{3}$

3 $h = 2 \cdot 5$ metres

4 The pile is driven $\dfrac{h}{10}$ into the ground.

296
DS

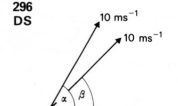

Two particles are simultaneously projected from the same point as shown. What is the numerical value of the distance between them one second later ? (The value of g is NOT given.)

1 $\alpha + \beta = 60°$

2 $\alpha - \beta = 45°$

297
DS

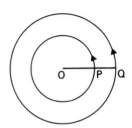

ω_1 and ω_2 are the constant angular velocities of OP and OQ respectively. The initial position is shown. Find the numerical value of the least time which elapses before O, P, Q are again collinear.

1 $\omega_1 - \omega_2 = 4$ radians per second.
2 The ratio of the radii is $2 : 1$.

298 S is a system of coplanar forces which are not in equilibrium. Does it
DS reduce to a couple ?

1 There are three points in the plane about which S has equal moments.
2 There is a direction in which the resolute of S is zero.

299
DS

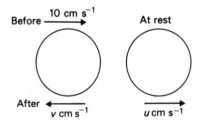

The two spheres impinge directly. Find the numerical value of e.

1 $u - v = 1$ **2** $u + v = 5$

PAPER 30

300 What is the ratio of the volumes into which a uniform right circular cone is divided by a plane parallel to its base through its centroid ?

A $27 : 64$ **C** $8 : 27$ **E** $1 : 1$
B $27 : 37$ **D** $8 : 19$

301

When this system, consisting of two equal masses and two identical elastic strings, is hanging in equilibrium the ratio of the energy in the upper string to that in the lower is

A 4 : 1   **C** 1 : 1   **E** 1 : 4
B 2 : 1   **D** 1 : 2

302 In this question all speeds are in kmh⁻¹ units.
An aircraft is heading in the direction $3\mathbf{i} - 4\mathbf{j}$, $\mathbf{i}$ and $\mathbf{j}$ being horizontal unit vectors, and has airspeed 100. A wind is blowing with velocity $-5\mathbf{i} + 20\mathbf{j}$. The velocity of the aircraft relative to the ground is

A $55\mathbf{i} - 60\mathbf{j}$ **C** $65\mathbf{i} - 60\mathbf{j}$ **E** $305\mathbf{i} - 420\mathbf{j}$
B $60\mathbf{i} - 40\mathbf{j}$ **D** $295\mathbf{i} - 380\mathbf{j}$

303 If the units of mass, length and time are redefined to have twice their present values, the coherent unit of work will be equivalent to k joules where k is

A $\frac{1}{4}$ **C** 1   **E** 4
B $\frac{1}{2}$ **D** 2

304 A body is resting on horizontal ground and λ is the angle of friction between the two surfaces in contact. It is to be moved by applying to it as small a force as possible. In what direction must the force be applied?

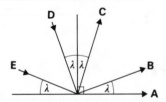

305

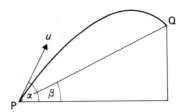

Express tan β in terms of u, α, g and t, where t is the time of flight from P to Q.

A $\dfrac{2u \sin \alpha - gt}{2u \cos \alpha}$ **C** $\dfrac{2u \cos \alpha - gt}{2u \sin \alpha}$ **E** $\dfrac{2u \sin \alpha + gt}{2u \cos \alpha}$

B $\dfrac{u \sin \alpha - gt}{u \cos \alpha}$ **D** $\dfrac{u \sin \alpha + gt}{u \cos \alpha}$

306 The dimensions of a physical quantity are expressed in the form
MC $M^{\alpha} L^{\beta} T^{\gamma}$. $\alpha + \beta + \gamma = 0$ for

1 force   **2** velocity   **3** power

307
MC

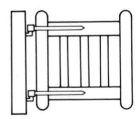

The forces on this garden gate, which is open but not swinging, are such that

1 the vertical forces at the hinges form a couple
2 the horizontal forces at the hinges form a couple
3 the weight and the vertical forces at the hinges reduce to a couple

61

308 The centroid of a tetrahedron, not necessarily regular, made of material
MC of uniform density, coincides with that of

> **1** 4 particles of equal mass placed at its vertices
> **2** 6 particles of equal mass placed at the mid-points of its sides
> **3** 4 particles of equal mass placed at the centroids of its faces

309 **u** is the initial velocity of a projectile and **v** is its velocity at time t. If
MC **u** and **v** are represented by vectors $\overline{OP}$ and $\overline{OQ}$ respectively, then

> **1** $v = u + gt$ **2** Q is vertically below P
> **3** PQ increases at a constant rate

PAPER 31

310 P is a particle.
RA
> **1** The velocity of P is zero.
> **2** The resultant force acting on P is zero.

311
RA

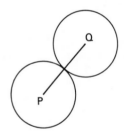

The circle centre Q rolls without slipping on the equal fixed circle
centre P.

> **1** PQ makes one revolution.
> **2** The circle centre Q makes one revolution.

312 An equilateral triangle XYZ and a circle S lie in the same plane. P is a
RA point on S.

> **1** The magnitude of the resultant of the forces $\overline{PX}$, $\overline{PY}$, $\overline{PZ}$ is constant.
> **2** S is the circumcircle of the triangle.

313
DN A train is travelling along a level track. What is the frictional resistance in newtons per tonne ?

1 The mass of the train is 120 tonnes.
2 The engine is working at 250 kW.
3 The speed is 25 kmh $^{-1}$.
4 The acceleration is $0 \cdot 2$ ms^{-2}.

314
DN

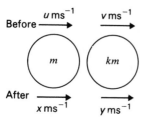

The coefficient of restitution between these directly impinging spheres is e. Find x.

1 $u = 2$ **2** $v = 1$ **3** $e = \frac{1}{2}$ **4** $k = 2$

315
DN g is determined experimentally using a conical pendulum. What is its value ?

1 The period of one revolution is 1 s.
2 The mass of the bob is 1 kg.
3 The radius of the circular path is $\frac{1}{4}$ m.
4 The angle of inclination of the string is 45°.

316
DN

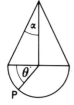

The diagram shows a section through the axis of a body consisting of a solid cone fastened to a solid hemisphere. Can the body rest in equilibrium with the point P in contact with a horizontal plane ?

1 Both parts of the body are uniform.
2 $\tan \alpha = \frac{1}{3}$ **3** $\theta = 30°$
4 The average density of the hemisphere is three times that of the cone.

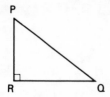

A body starts from rest at P and slides down the smooth fixed plane. What is its speed on reaching Q ? (Take $g = 10$ ms^{-2})

1 PR = 30 cm   **2** RQ = 40 cm

318 A car travels with constant speed 20 ms^{-1} in a horizontal circle of radius
DS 100 metres round a banked circular race track. Taking g as 10 ms^{-2}, what is the resultant force acting on the car ?

1 The mass of the car is 1000 kg.
2 There is no tendency to sideslip.

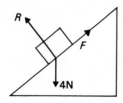

The body of weight 4N is in limiting equilibrium on the fixed plane. What is the value of the coefficient of friction between it and the plane ?

1 $R = 2\sqrt{3}$ N   **2** $F = 2$ N

PAPER 32

320

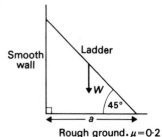

Smooth wall — Ladder — W — 45° — a — Rough ground. $\mu = 0.2$

What is the least couple which, applied to the uniform ladder, will keep it in the position shown ?

A $1 \cdot 2\,Wa$　　C $0 \cdot 7\,Wa$　　E $0 \cdot 3\,Wa$
B $0 \cdot 8\,Wa$　　D $0 \cdot 5\,Wa$

321

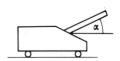

The gun of mass M fires a shell of mass m and is free to recoil horizontally. The angle of elevation of the shell as it leaves the barrel is

A greater than α and decreases with M
B greater than α and increases with M
C less than α and decreases with M
D less than α and increases with M
E equal to α and is thus independent of M

322 A mass is hanging in a lift, being suspended by a light inextensible string. The lift ascends, first moving with uniform acceleration, then with uniform speed, finally retarding to rest with a retardation of the same magnitude as the acceleration. Given that the tension, T, is greater than zero throughout, what is the form of its graph against time, t, during the three parts of the motion ?

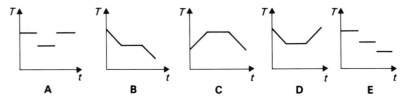

323

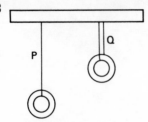

Two identical rings are suspended from a beam by means of identical elastic strings. In case P, one end of the string is tied to the beam and the other end to the ring. In case Q, both ends are tied to a point in the beam, the string passing through the ring. The rings, initially supported with the strings just taut, are slowly lowered until they hang freely. The ratio of the distances through which they are lowered (P : Q) is

A 1 : 4   **C** 1 : 1   **E** 4 : 1
B 1 : 2   **D** 2 : 1

324 The velocity of a ship is given by the vector 20**i** and the velocity of the wind is —4**i** + 3**j**, **i** and **j** being horizontal vectors. The direction of the smoke trail from the funnel is that of the vector

A 16**i** + 3**j**   **C** – 24**i** + 3**j**   **E** – 4**i** + 3**j**
B – 16**i** – 3**j**   **D** 24**i** – 3**j**

325 A smooth, rigid, circular wire ring is made to rotate with uniform angular velocity about a diameter which is vertical. The number of points on the ring where a small heavy bead threaded on the wire can remain at relative rest is

A 1   **B** 2   **C** 3   **D** 4   **E** 6

326
MC

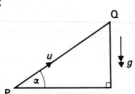

A particle at P is fired with speed u in the direction PQ at the same instant as a second particle at Q is released to fall from rest. In order to determine whether the two particles collide it is NOT necessary to know the magnitudes of

1 u **2** α **3** PQ

327
MC The dimensions of a physical quantity are expressed in the form $M^\alpha L^\beta T^\gamma$. $\alpha + \beta + \gamma = -1$ for

1 impulse   **2** angular velocity   **3** acceleration

328
MC A body moving in a straight line has initial velocity u and initial acceleration $a \ (> 0)$ which increases with time. If after time t the velocity has increased to v and the body has covered a distance s then

1 $v > u + at$ **2** $s > ut + \frac{1}{2}at^2$ **3** $s > \frac{u+v}{2}t$

329
MC

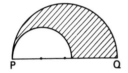

From a uniform semicircular lamina of radius a is cut a semicircular piece of radius ka $(k < 1)$ as shown. When the shaded part is freely suspended from P the angle which PQ makes with the vertical is independent of

1 g **2** a **3** k

PAPER 33

330
RA In a consistent system of units the velocity, acceleration and momentum of a rigid body are specified by the non-zero vectors **v**, **a** and **p** respectively. **F** is the resultant force acting on it.

1 $\mathbf{p} = \mathbf{v}$ **2** $\mathbf{F} = \mathbf{a}$

331
RA A particle P is moving in two dimensions.
  1 The path of P is circular.
  2 The acceleration of P is directed towards a fixed point.

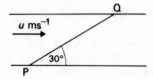

The river flows at u ms^{-1} and a man who rows at v ms^{-1} relative to the water wishes to cross in a straight line from P to Q.

1 $2v > u$
2 There are two possible directions in which he can row.

333
DN

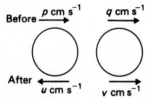

In this direct impact between two spheres, p and q are the roots of $x^2 + ax + b = 0$ and u and v are the roots of $x^2 + cx + d = 0$. What is the numerical value of the coefficient of restitution ?

1 $a = -8$ **3** $c = -5$
2 $b = 7$ **4** $d = 6$

334 The string of a conical pendulum is light. What angle does it make with
DN the vertical ?

1 The length of the string is 57 cm.
2 The mass of the bob is 10 grams.
3 The bob makes 7 revolutions per second.
4 The value of g is $9 \cdot 8$ ms^{-2}.

**335
DN**

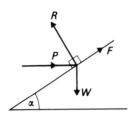

A particle of weight W is maintained in equilibrium on a slope of angle α by means of a horizontal force P. F is the frictional force. What is the numerical value of P ?

1 $\alpha = 30°$.
2 The coefficient of friction is $\frac{1}{9}\sqrt{3}$.
3 The normal contact force R is $3\sqrt{3}$ N.
4 The weight W is 5 N.

**336
DS** A bus moves from rest with uniform acceleration a ms^{-2}. A man, initially x metres behind the bus, runs after it with constant speed u ms^{-1} and just catches it after 6 seconds. What is the value of u ?

1 $x = 27$ **2** $a = 1 \cdot 5$

**337
DS**

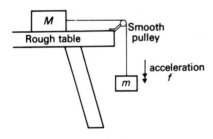

The masses are in motion in a vertical plane. What is the numerical value of the coefficient of friction between mass M and the table ?

1 $m = 2M$ **2** $f = \frac{5g}{8}$

338 *F* is the least horizontal force which will prevent a small body of weight
DS 3N from sliding down a fixed rough plane of angle 45°. Were this force
increased to *F ′* the body would be on the point of sliding up the plane.
What is the numerical value of μ ?

1 $F = 1N$ **2** $F' = 9N$

339 Two particles P, Q of masses *m, km* are connected by a light string
DS passing over a smooth fixed pulley. The parts of the string not in contact
with the pulley are vertical. Given *g*, what is the tension in the string ?

1 $k = 2$ **2** The acceleration of P is $\frac{g}{3}$

PAPER 34

340

The pulley has radius *a* and a frictional couple of maximum magnitude
$2mga$ can be called into play at its rough axle. What is the range of
values which *k* can take if the system is to remain at rest ?

A $5 < k < 7$ **C** $5 < k < 9$ **E** $1 < k < 9$
B $3 < k < 7$ **D** $1 < k < 5$

341 A uniform right circular cone of mass 40 grams, semi-vertical angle 30°
and slant length 40 cm, rests with its base on a smooth horizontal table.
A small particle of mass 10 grams is just displaced from its vertex.
When it reaches the table the distance through which the cone has
moved is

A   4 cm   **C**   15 cm   **E**   20 cm
B   5 cm   **D**   16 cm

342 Two identical uniform rods, KH and HL, of length 24 cm are freely hinged together at H and are to rest end to end in a horizontal line on two supports, one of them at K. What is the distance between the supports ?

A 48 cm   **C** 32 cm   **E** 28 cm
B 36 cm   **D** 30 cm

343

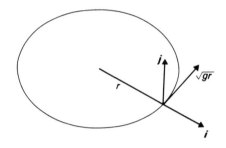

A bead of mass m is moving with speed $\sqrt{gr}$ on a smooth horizontal circular wire of radius r. The unit vector $\mathbf{j}$ is vertically upwards. The force which the bead exerts on the wire is in the direction of

A $-\mathbf{j}$ **C** $-\mathbf{i}+\mathbf{j}$ **E** $\mathbf{i}+\mathbf{j}$
B $-\mathbf{i}-\mathbf{j}$ **D** $\mathbf{i}-\mathbf{j}$

344

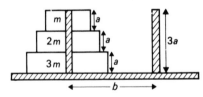

The three discs, each with a small central hole, are to be transferred one at a time from the left hand pillar to the right, the order of the discs being reversed. What is the least amount of work which has to be done to effect the transfer ?

A $14\,mga$ **C** $11\,mga$ **E** $4\,mga+6\,mgb$
B $14\,mga+6\,mgb$ **D** $4\,mga$

345

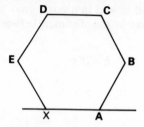

The diagram shows the vertical cross-section through the centre of a uniform regular hexagonal prism resting on very rough horizontal ground. In order to make the prism turn about its edge through X by using as small a force as possible, at which vertex must the force be applied ?

346 MC

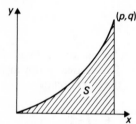

If $\bar{y}$ is the y co-ordinate of the centroid of the area S then $S\bar{y} =$

1 $\int_0^p (q - y) x \, \mathrm{d}x$ **2** $\int_0^q (p - x) y \, \mathrm{d}y$ **3** $\int_0^p \frac{y^2}{2} \, \mathrm{d}x$

347 MC

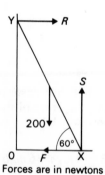

Forces are in newtons

The diagram shows a uniform ladder resting on rough horizontal ground and against a smooth vertical wall. Equations, sufficient to determine F, R and S, can be found by

1 resolving vertically and taking moments about X and Y

2 taking moments about X, Y and O

3 resolving horizontally, vertically and in the direction XY

348
MC

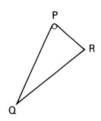

The diagram shows a uniform rod QR of weight W supported by two strings tied to its ends and to a fixed point P. In equilibrium it is necessary that

1 the mid-point of the rod is vertically below P

2 the resultant of the tensions acting at P is a force W vertically upwards

3 the tensions in the strings are equal

349 A couple
MC

1 has the same dimensions as work

2 may be measured in newton-metre units

3 has the same moment about all axes perpendicular to its plane

Further Mathematics

Pure

PAPER 35

350 When expanded, $\cosh(x + y) \equiv$

    A $\cosh x + \cosh y$
    B $\cosh x - \cosh y$
    C $\cosh x \sinh y + \sinh x \cosh y$
    D $\cosh x \cosh y + \sinh x \sinh y$
    E $\cosh x \cosh y - \sinh x \sinh y$

351 α is a first approximation to $^n\sqrt{k}$. A closer approximation, obtained by applying Newton's method once to $x^n - k = 0$ is $\alpha + \epsilon$, where $\epsilon =$

    A $-\dfrac{(\alpha^n - k)}{n\,\alpha^{n-1}}$
        D $\dfrac{n\,\alpha^{n-1}}{\alpha^n - k}$

    B $\dfrac{\alpha^n - k}{n\,\alpha^{n-1}}$
        E $-\dfrac{(\alpha^n + k)}{n\,\alpha^{n-1}}$

    C $-\dfrac{n\,\alpha^{n-1}}{\alpha^n - k}$

352 The sum of the squares of the roots of the equation

$$2x^3 + 3x^2 - 3x + 5 = 0$$

is equal to

    A $-2\frac{3}{4}$
        C $-2\frac{1}{4}$
        E 9
    B $-\frac{3}{4}$
        D $5\frac{1}{4}$

353 If $x + 1$ is a factor of $x^3 - ax^2 - 5x - 6$, what is the value of a ?

    A -12
        C -2
        E 10
    B -10
        D 2

354 When $\lg x = y \lg 3 + 1$ is expressed in a form not involving logs it becomes $x =$

A 10.3^y **C** $3^y + 10$ **E** $10y^3$

B 30^y **D** $y^3 + 10$

355 $\int \dfrac{dx}{9 + 4x^2}$ is

A $\dfrac{1}{9} \arctan \dfrac{2x}{9} + c$ **D** $9 \arctan \dfrac{2x}{9} + c$

B $\dfrac{1}{3} \arctan \dfrac{2x}{3} + c$ **E** $\dfrac{3}{2} \arctan \dfrac{2x}{3} + c$

C $\dfrac{1}{6} \arctan \dfrac{2x}{3} + c$

356 The coefficient of x^2 in the expansion of

$$(1 + ax) \ln(1 + x)$$

will be zero if a is

A -1 **C** 0 **E** 1

B $-\frac{1}{2}$ **D** $\frac{1}{2}$

357

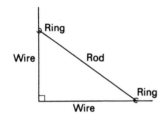

The locus of the centre of the rod as the rings move on the wires is part of

A   a straight line   **C**   an ellipse   **E**   a hyperbola

B   a circle   **D**   a parabola

358 Which of the following is the converse of the proposition " If P is true then Q is false " ?

  A If P is false then Q is true.
  B If P is false then Q is false.
  C If P is true then Q is true.
  D If Q is false then P is true.
  E If Q is true then P is false.

359 The magnitude of the vector $3\mathbf{i} + 4\mathbf{j} - 5\mathbf{k}$ is

  A 0   **B** $\sqrt{2}$ **C** 2   **D** $5\sqrt{2}$ **E** 50

PAPER 36

360
MC Which of the following are even functions of x ?

  1 $x^3\sinh x$ **2** $x \cosh x$ **3** $x^2\, e^x$

361
MC The graph of $y = |x - 2| + |x + 2|$

  1 is symmetrical about the x-axis
  2 consists of two straight lines
  3 has zero gradient at $x = 1$

362
MC Of which of the following functions is the derivative e^{2x} ?

  1 $e^x \cosh x$ **2** $e^x\sinh x$ **3** e^{2x}

363
MC

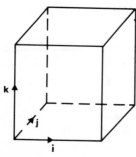

Which of the following vectors can be represented by a diagonal of the unit cube ?

  1 $\mathbf{i} - \mathbf{j} + \mathbf{k}$ **2** $\mathbf{i} - \mathbf{j} - \mathbf{k}$ **3** $\mathbf{i} + \mathbf{j} + \mathbf{k}$

364
MC The hyperbolas $\dfrac{x^2}{a^2} - \dfrac{y^2}{b^2} = 1$ and $\dfrac{x^2}{a^2} - \dfrac{y^2}{b^2} = -1$ have the same

1 asymptotes   **2** eccentricity   **3** directrices

365
MC The triangle in the Argand diagram with vertices which represent the complex numbers z, ωz and $\omega^2 z$ (where ω is a complex cube root of unity)

1 is equilateral
2 has its centroid at the origin
3 has area $\dfrac{3\sqrt{3}}{4} |z|^2$

366
MC For which of the following integrals is a hyperbolic substitution a suitable one to make ?

1 $\displaystyle\int \dfrac{dx}{\sqrt{(a^2 - x^2)}}$ **2** $\displaystyle\int \dfrac{dx}{\sqrt{(x^2 - a^2)}}$ **3** $\displaystyle\int \dfrac{dx}{\sqrt{(a^2 + x^2)}}$

367
MC The equation $4x^3 - 12x^2 - x + 3 = 0$

1 has a root between 1 and 2
2 has a root between -1 and 0
3 has three real roots

368
MC To express $f(x) \equiv \dfrac{2}{4x^2 + 8x + 3}$ as $\dfrac{1}{2x + 1} - \dfrac{1}{2x + 3}$

would be a suitable first stage in finding

1 $\displaystyle\sum_{x=1}^{n} f(x)$
2 the coefficient of x^{10} in the expansion of $f(x)$ in ascending powers of x
3 $\displaystyle\int f(x)\, dx$

369
MC The complete area enclosed by the curve $r^2 = a^2 \cos 2\theta$ can be evaluated from $\displaystyle\int_0^\alpha k r^2\, d\theta$ where α, k are respectively

1 $2\pi, \frac{1}{2}$ **2** $\pi, 1$ **3** $\pi/4, 2$

PAPER 37

370 Find the coefficient of x^3 in the expansion of $\exp(x - x^2)$.

- **A** -1
- **B** $-\frac{5}{6}$
- **C** $-\frac{2}{3}$
- **D** $\frac{1}{6}$
- **E** $\frac{1}{3}$

371 The sine of the acute angle between the vectors $\mathbf{i} + \mathbf{j}$ and $\mathbf{i} - \mathbf{k}$ is

- **A** 0
- **B** $\frac{1}{2}$
- **C** $\frac{1}{\sqrt{2}}$
- **D** $\frac{\sqrt{3}}{2}$
- **E** 1

372 Which of the following transformations, if any, is equivalent to reflecting a point first in $y = x$ and then in $y = -x$?

- **A** The identity transformation.
- **B** Reflection in the origin.
- **C** Reflection in the x-axis.
- **D** Reflection in the y-axis.
- **E** None of these.

373 Below there is a proof, which may be fallacious, that $6^n - 5n + 3$ is a multiple of 5 for all positive integral values of n. At which stage, if any, does the first error occur ?

$f(n + 1) \equiv 6^{n+1} - 5n - 2$
stage 1

$f(n + 1) - f(n) \equiv 6^{n+1} - 6^n - 5$
stage 2

$\equiv 5(6^n - 1),$
stage 3

Hence $f(n)$ is a multiple of 5 for all integral values of n.
stage 4

- **A** stage 1
- **B** stage 2
- **C** stage 3
- **D** stage 4
- **E** None of these : there is no error.

374 The tangent at $(a \cos \theta, b \sin \theta)$ to the ellipse $\dfrac{x^2}{a^2} + \dfrac{y^2}{b^2} = 1$ has equation

- **A** $bx \cos \theta + ay \sin \theta = 1$
- **B** $ax \cos \theta + by \sin \theta = 1$
- **C** $bx \cos \theta + ay \sin \theta = ab$
- **D** $ax \cos \theta + by \sin \theta = a^2b^2$
- **E** $ax \cos \theta + by \sin t = a^2\cos^2 \theta + b^2\sin^2 \theta$

375 The sum of the reciprocals of the roots of the equation

$$2x^3 - 3x^2 - 4x + 3 = 0$$

is equal to

A $-\frac{4}{3}$ **C** $-\frac{2}{3}$ **E** $\frac{4}{3}$
B -1 **D** $\frac{2}{3}$

376
MC $\mathbf{p} = \mathbf{i} - \mathbf{j} + \mathbf{k}$ $\mathbf{q} = 2\mathbf{i} + \mathbf{j} - \mathbf{k}$ $\mathbf{r} = \mathbf{j} + \mathbf{k}$

Which of the following pairs of vectors are perpendicular ?

1 $\mathbf{q}$ and $\mathbf{r}$ **2** $\mathbf{r}$ and $\mathbf{p}$ **3** $\mathbf{p}$ and $\mathbf{q}$

377 Which of the following functions can be integrated with respect to x
MC to give an inverse sine function plus a constant ?

1 $(5 - 2x + x^2)^{-\frac{1}{2}}$ **2** $(5 - 2x - x^2)^{-\frac{1}{2}}$ **3** $(5 + 2x - x^2)^{-\frac{1}{2}}$

378 The curve $y^2 = x^2(4 - x^2)$ has two
MC
1 axes of symmetry in its plane
2 loops
3 tangents at the origin

379 If $f(n) \equiv g(n + 1) - g(n)$ where $g(1) = 0$ and $g(n) \to a$ as $n \to \infty$ then
MC
1 $f(0) = 0$ **2** $f(n) \to 0$ as $n \to \infty$ **3** $\sum\limits_{n=1}^{\infty} f(n) = a$

PAPER 38

380) α is an approximation to a root of $f(x) = 0$.
RA
1 β is a better approximation to the root.
2 $\beta = \alpha - \dfrac{f(\alpha)}{f'(\alpha)}$

381 $p(x)$ and $q(x)$ are polynomials. $a \neq 0$.
RA
1 $p(x)$ and $q(x)$ leave the same remainder on division by $x - a$.
2 $xp(x) - aq(a)$ is divisible by $x - a$.

382
RA **1** $\int_a^b \dfrac{dx}{x}$ can be evaluated.   **2** $ab < 0$

383 **P** and **Q** are any two matrices.
RA
    1 The products **PQ** and **QP** can both be formed.
    2 **P** and **Q** are square and of the same order.

384 **1** The points with co-ordinates (p, q), (r, s), (t, u) are collinear.
RA **2** $\begin{vmatrix} p & q & 1 \\ r & s & 1 \\ t & u & 1 \end{vmatrix} = 0$

385 Find the number of real points of intersection of the curves
DN
$$x^2 + y^2 + 2gx + c = 0 \quad \text{and} \quad \frac{x^2}{a^2} + \frac{y^2}{b^2} = 1.$$

    1 $g = 7$ **3** $a = 8$
    2 $c = 6$ **4** $b = 5$

386 Find the numerical value of the sum of the cubes of the roots of the
DN equation $x^4 + ax^3 + bx^2 + cx + d = 0$.

    1 $a = 1$ **3** $c = 3$
    2 $b = 2$ **4** $d = 4$

387 P is a point on an ellipse with foci H, K and PH + PK = 8. What is the
DS eccentricity of the ellipse ?

    1 The distance between the foci is 4.
    2 The distance between the directrices is 16.

388 Is a snark a boojum ?
DS   **1** All boojums are snarks.   **2** No boojum is not a snark.

389 Determine the constants a and b in the differential equation
DS
$$\frac{d^2y}{dx^2} + a\frac{dy}{dx} + by = 12x - 28.$$

    1 The particular integral is $2x - 3$.
    2 The complementary function is of the form $pe^{2x} + qe^{3x}$.

PAPER 39

390 Let $P = \begin{bmatrix} 2 & -1 \\ 3 & 2 \end{bmatrix}$, $Q = \begin{bmatrix} 4 & 2 \\ 6 & 5 \end{bmatrix}$, $R = \begin{bmatrix} 2 & 1 \\ -3 & 2 \end{bmatrix}$ and $X = PQR$.

The number of zero elements in X is

A 0   C 2   E 4
B 1   D 3

391 Four of the points   A $(2, -1, 1)$,   B $(3, -2, 1)$,   C $(-2, 1, 2)$, D $(-1, -2, -3)$ and E $(-1, 2, -1)$ lie on the same side of the plane $3x + 4y - 2z = 1$. Which is the odd-man-out ?

392 In three dimensions the vector equation $(r - a) \cdot (r - b) = 0$ where **a** and **b** are unequal constant vectors, represents

A a pair of points   D a pair of spheres
B a pair of straight lines   E none of these
C a pair of circles

393 Taking $x = \dfrac{\pi}{2}$ as an approximate root of the equation $\cot x = mx$, where m is small, the closer approximation obtained by using Newton's method once is

A $\dfrac{\pi}{2(1 - m)}$ C $\dfrac{\pi}{2} - \dfrac{2(1 + m)}{\pi m}$ E $\dfrac{\pi(1 - 2m)}{2(1 - m)}$

B $\dfrac{\pi}{2(1 + m)}$ D $\dfrac{\pi(1 + 2m)}{2(1 + m)}$

394 A rumour is started by one person in a village of 10 000 inhabitants and everyone who hears it passes it on indiscriminately to eight other people in each hour. (Some of these may have heard it already.) After t hours there are z people who have heard the rumour. Which of the following expressions gives the best approximation to $\dfrac{dz}{dt}$ during the first few hours ?

A 8   C $8 - 0 \cdot 0008z$ E $8z - 0 \cdot 0008z^2$
B $8z$ D $8z - 0 \cdot 008z^2$

395 Which of the following sketch graphs is that of the function

$$\frac{x}{(x-1)(x+2)} \ ?$$

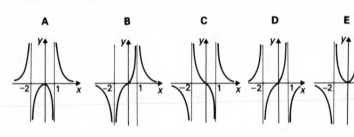

396 x and y are real.
MC The expression e^{nz} is equal to

1 $\cos ny + i \sin ny$ when $z = iy$
2 $\cosh nx + i \sinh nx$ when $z = x$
3 $e^{nx}(\cos y + i \sin y)$ when $z = x + iy$

397 If **P** is any non-singular 2×2 matrix then
MC

1 $\left[\mathbf{P}^{\mathrm{T}}\right]^{\mathrm{T}} = \left[\mathbf{P}^{-1}\right]^{-1}$ **2** $\left[\mathbf{P}^{\mathrm{T}}\right]^{-1} = \left[\mathbf{P}^{-1}\right]^{\mathrm{T}}$ **3** $|\mathbf{P}^{\mathrm{T}}| = |\mathbf{P}^{-1}|$

398 **a**, **b**, **c** are three vectors having the same non-zero magnitude. Which of
MC the following CANNOT be true ?

1 $\mathbf{a}.\mathbf{b} = \mathbf{c}$ **2** $\mathbf{a} \times \mathbf{b} = \mathbf{c}$ **3** $\mathbf{a} + \mathbf{b} = \mathbf{c}$

399
MC

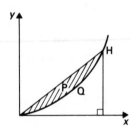

H is the point with parameter h on the curve $x = at^n$, $y = at^m$. $(m > n > 0)$.
The ratio of the volumes produced when the areas P and Q are rotated
through an angle α about the x-axis is independent of

1 a **2** α **3** h

PAPER 40

400 $f(x)$ is a continuous function.
RA **1** $f(a).f(b) \geqslant 0$
2 There are no roots of $f(x) = 0$ between a and b.

401 $\qquad S_n = \sum_{r=1}^{n} u_r$
RA
1 As $n \to \infty$, $S_n \to S$
2 As $n \to \infty$, $u_n \to u$

402 $\mathbf{P} \in S$, the set of all matrices of the form $\begin{bmatrix} 1 & x \\ 0 & 1 \end{bmatrix}$.
RA
1 $\mathbf{PQ} = \mathbf{I}$ **2** $\mathbf{Q} \in S$

403 H, K are the points $(-1,0)$, $(1,0)$ respectively and P is a variable
RA point (x, y).

1 $|PH - PK| = 3$
2 The locus of P is a hyperbola.

404 **1** $\mathbf{p}, \mathbf{q}, \mathbf{r}$ will serve as basis vectors in three dimensions.
RA **2** $\mathbf{p}, \mathbf{q}, \mathbf{r}$ can be represented by the sides of a triangle taken in order.

405 Find the numerical value of the determinant $\begin{vmatrix} 1 & pq & 1 \\ r & 1 & q \\ s & q & 1 \end{vmatrix}$.
DN

1 $p = 1$ **3** $r = 3$
2 $q = 2$ **4** $s = 4$

406 Is $x + 2$ a factor of $\quad pqx^3 + qrx^2 + rsx + sp$?
DN
1 $p = 1$ **3** $r = 3$
2 $q = 2$ **4** $s = 4$

407 Is S true ?
DN
1 $Q \Rightarrow (P \Rightarrow S)$ **3** $S \Rightarrow P$
2 $P \Rightarrow (R \Rightarrow Q)$ **4** $R \Rightarrow \sim Q$

408 Is $b^2c^2 + c^2a^2 + a^2b^2$ a perfect square ?
DS
1 $a + b + c = 0$ **2** $a - b - c = 0$

409 $p(x)$ is a cubic polynomial. Does $p(x) = 0$ have three distinct roots ?

DS

1 $p(x) = 0$ and $p'(x) = 0$ have a common root.

2 The x-axis and the graph of $y = p(x)$ divide the plane into 5 regions.

PAPER 41

410 Two of the direction cosines of a line are $\frac{1}{2}$ and $-\frac{1}{4}$. The third one is

A $\dfrac{11}{16}$

C $\dfrac{\sqrt{11}}{4}$

E not necessarily any of these

B $\dfrac{3}{4}$

D $\dfrac{\sqrt{13}}{4}$

411 If the perimeter of the astroid $x = \cos^3 t$, $y = \sin^3 t$ is expressed as $\int_0^{\frac{\pi}{2}} f(t)\,dt$ then $f(t)$ is

A $36 \sin^2 t \cos^2 t$ **C** $12 \sin t \cos t$ **E** $3 \sin t \cos t$

B $18 \sin^2 t \cos^2 t$ **D** $6 \sin t \cos t$

412 Assuming ONLY that all questions in this book were composed either by Payne or by Pennycuick and that all the latter's questions are sound, a necessary conclusion is that

A some of Payne's questions are faulty
B this question was composed by Pennycuick
C all faulty questions were composed by Payne
D Pennycuick failed to find the errors in Payne's questions
E the book contains faulty questions

413

$$X = \begin{bmatrix} 3 & 5 \\ -1 & -2 \end{bmatrix} \quad X^{-1} \text{ is}$$

A $\begin{bmatrix} 2 & 5 \\ -1 & -3 \end{bmatrix}$

C $\begin{bmatrix} \frac{1}{3} & \frac{1}{5} \\ -1 & -\frac{1}{2} \end{bmatrix}$

E $\begin{bmatrix} 3 & -1 \\ -5 & -2 \end{bmatrix}$

B $\begin{bmatrix} -2 & -5 \\ 1 & 3 \end{bmatrix}$

D $\begin{bmatrix} -3 & -1 \\ 5 & 2 \end{bmatrix}$

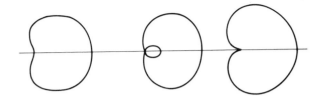

The labels

P: $\boxed{r = 1 + \cos\theta}$ Q: $\boxed{r = 2 + \cos\theta}$ R: $\boxed{r = 1 + 2\,\cos\theta}$

should be attached to the curves in the order

A Q R P	**C** P R Q	**E** Q P R
B R P Q	**D** R Q P	

415 In seeking a particular integral of the equation

$$\frac{d^2y}{dx^2} - 7\frac{dy}{dx} + 6y = e^x$$

which of the following forms should the trial function take ?

A $ae^{-x} + be^{-6x}$	**C** $ax + be^x$	**E** axe^x
B $ae^x + be^{6x}$	**D** ae^x	

416 The probability that P hits the bull with a single shot is $\frac{1}{2}$; the probability that Q does the same is $\frac{1}{4}$. P has 2 shots and Q has 4. The ratio of their probabilities (P : Q) of hitting the bull at least once is

A $64:27$	**C** $32:27$	**E** $64:85$
B $2:1$	**D** $192:175$	

417
MC If $\mathbf{r}, \mathbf{a}, \mathbf{b}$ are coplanar vectors, $\mathbf{r}.\mathbf{a} = \mathbf{r}.\mathbf{b}$ and $\mathbf{r} \neq 0$, then

1 $\mathbf{a}$ and $\mathbf{b}$ have equal components perpendicular to $\mathbf{r}$
2 $\mathbf{a}$ and $\mathbf{b}$ have equal components parallel to $\mathbf{r}$
3 if $\mathbf{a} \neq \mathbf{b}$, $\mathbf{r}$ is perpendicular to $\mathbf{a} - \mathbf{b}$

418
MC If $x^3 - px + q$ has a repeated factor $x - a$ then

    1 $p = 3a^2$
    2 $q = 2a^3$
    3 the third factor is $x + 2a$

419
MC Which of the following functions can be integrated with respect to x to give an inverse hyperbolic function plus a constant ?

    1 $(x^2 + 4x + 7)^{\frac{1}{2}}$ **2** $(x^2 + 4x - 7)^{\frac{1}{2}}$ **3** $(x^2 - 4x - 7)^{\frac{1}{2}}$

PAPER 42

420
RA **1** $f(x)$ is periodic with period a.
    2 $f(x + a) \equiv f(x)$

421
RA **1** The roots of the equation $\begin{vmatrix} a+z & b \\ c & d+z \end{vmatrix} = 0$ are complex.
    2 b and c are of opposite sign.

422
RA The equation of the pair of tangents from the origin to the circle S is $ax^2 + 2hxy + by^2 = 0$

    1 $h = 0$ **2** S has its centre on the x-axis.

423
RA L is a straight line.

    1 L touches the hyperbola $xy = 1$.
    2 The triangle formed by L and the co-ordinate axes has area 4 square units.

424
RA ω is a complex cube root of unity and P, Q, R are the points in an Argand diagram representing the complex numbers p, q, r respectively.

    1 $\triangle$ PQR is equilateral.   **2** $\omega(q - p) = r - q$

425
DN The parabola $y^2 = 4ax$ meets the line $bx + cy + d = 0$ in real points P, Q, and O is the origin. Is $< POQ = \frac{\pi}{2}$?

    1 $a = 1$ **3** $c = 3$
    2 $b = 2$ **4** $d = -7$

426
DN Is $x^2 - a^2$ a factor of $f(x)$?

    1 $f(x)$ is a polynomial.   **3** $f(x) + f(-x) \equiv 0$
    2 $f(a) = 0$ **4** $f(a^2) = 0$

427 $f_r(x)$ denotes the r th derivative of $f(x)$ with respect to x.
DN Does $f(x)$ have a maximum at $x = 2$?

1 $f_1(2) = 0$ 3 $f_3(2) = 0$
2 $f_2(2) = 0$ 4 $f_4(2) = -1$

428 Does $P \Rightarrow Q$?
DS
1 $\sim Q \Rightarrow \sim P$ 2 $\sim P \Rightarrow \sim Q$

429 Find the numerical value of the determinant
DS

$$\begin{vmatrix} p^2 & 2p & 1 \\ q^2 & 2q & 1 \\ pq & p+q & 1 \end{vmatrix}$$

1 $p + q = 7$ 2 $p - q = 3$

PAPER 43

430
In this question $\mathbf{I} = \begin{bmatrix} 1 & 0 \\ 0 & 1 \end{bmatrix}$, $\mathbf{O} = \begin{bmatrix} 0 & 0 \\ 0 & 0 \end{bmatrix}$ and

$\mathbf{X}$ is a 2×2 matrix such that $\mathbf{X}^2 = \mathbf{I}$. Which step, if any, of the following argument is the first to contain an error ?

$\mathbf{X}^2 = \mathbf{I}$
$\mathbf{X}^2 - \mathbf{I}^2 = \mathbf{O}$ Step 1
$(\mathbf{X} - \mathbf{I})(\mathbf{X} + \mathbf{I}) = \mathbf{O}$ Step 2
$\mathbf{X} - \mathbf{I} = \mathbf{O}$ or $\mathbf{X} + \mathbf{I} = \mathbf{O}$ Step 3
$\mathbf{X} = \mathbf{I}$ or $\mathbf{X} = -\mathbf{I}$ Step 4

A Step 1   **C** Step 3   **E** There is no error.
B Step 2   **D** Step 4

431 H is the point $(4, -2, 3)$, K is the point $(2, 3, -1)$ and P divides HK in the ratio $\lambda : 1$. P lies on the plane $x - y + z = 3$.
What is the value of λ ?

A $\frac{2}{5}$ **C** $\frac{5}{6}$ **E** 3
B $\frac{5}{9}$ **D** $\frac{6}{5}$

432
$\displaystyle \mathop{\text{Lt}}_{n \to \infty} \left(\sum_{r=1}^{n} \frac{r^2}{n^3} \right)$ is

A 0   **C** $\frac{2}{3}$ **E** 2
B $\frac{1}{3}$ **D** 1

433 The four numbers 1, 2, 3, 4 are arranged as 2×2 determinant. How many different values are possible ?

A 3   C 5   E 7
B 4   D 6

434

$r = a(1+2\cos\theta)$

For the above curve, in which the area P does not include the area Q, $\int_0^{2\pi} \frac{1}{2} r^2 \, d\theta$ will give the area

A $P - 2Q$ C P E $P + 2Q$
B $P - Q$ D $P + Q$

435 If $f(x) = \sin x \cos(x - \alpha)$, then the period of $f(x)$ is

A α C π E 2π
B $\pi - \alpha$ D $2\pi - \alpha$

436 N, when expressed in prime factors, takes the form $a^p b^q c^r$. In how many ways can it be expressed as the product of two numbers ?

A $(p + 1)(q + 1)(r + 1)$
B $\frac{1}{2}(p + 1)(q + 1)(r + 1)$
C $\frac{1}{2}pqr$
D $\frac{1}{2}[(p + 1)(q + 1)(r + 1) + 1]$
E More information is needed.

437 If $\mathbf{r}$, $\mathbf{a}$, $\mathbf{b}$ are coplanar vectors, $\mathbf{r} \times \mathbf{a} = \mathbf{r} \times \mathbf{b}$ and $\mathbf{r} \neq 0$, then it can be
MC deduced that

1 $\mathbf{a}$ and $\mathbf{b}$ have equal components parallel to $\mathbf{r}$
2 $\mathbf{a}$ and $\mathbf{b}$ have equal components perpendicular to $\mathbf{r}$
3 if $\mathbf{a} \neq \mathbf{b}$ then $\mathbf{r}$ is parallel to $\mathbf{a} - \mathbf{b}$

438 If $k > 0$ is a sufficient condition for the truth of proposition P then
MC
1 if $k = -1$, P must be false
2 if P is false, k must be negative
3 if $k = 0$, P may be true

88

439 Defining cis θ to be $\cos \theta + i \sin \theta$

MC

  1 $\text{cis}(\theta + \phi) = \text{cis } \theta + \text{cis } \phi$

  2 $\text{cis}(-\theta) = -\text{cis } \theta$

  3 $(\text{cis } \theta)^n = \text{cis } n\theta$ (n is a positive integer)

PAPER 44

440 **1** $\sin x = \sin y$

RA **2** $\cosh x = \cosh y$

441 $p(x)$ is a polynomial.

RA

  1 $p(x) = 0$ has just one real root.

  2 $p(x) = 0$ has no real roots.

442 y is a function of x where $x = e^t$.

RA

  1 $\dfrac{d^2y}{dx^2} \equiv 0$ **2** $\dfrac{d^2y}{dt^2} \equiv \dfrac{dy}{dt}$

443 If $n > 1$ and $I_n = \int_0^{\frac{\pi}{2}} \sin^n \theta \, d\theta$ then $I_n = \dfrac{n-1}{n} I_{n-2}$.

RA

  1 When evaluated I_n contains a factor π.

  2 n is even.

444 For the differential equation $\dfrac{d^2y}{dx^2} + a\dfrac{dy}{dx} + by = 4x + 4$

RA

  1 the complementary function is of the form $pe^x + qe^{2x}$

  2 the particular integral is $2x - 1$

445 $p(x)$ and $q(x)$ are polynomials. In the graph of $y = \dfrac{p(x)}{q(x)}$, how many

DN asymptotes are there ?

  1 $p(x)$ and $q(x)$ are of the same degree.

  2 $p(x)$ and $q(x)$ have no common factor.

  3 $p(x) = 0$ for two real, distinct, values of x.

  4 $q(x) = 0$ for two real, distinct, values of x.

446 O is the origin and H, K are the points where the line $y = mx + c$ meets
DN the line pair $ax^2 + 2hxy + by^2 = 0$. Find the equation of the median of
the triangle OHK which passes through O.

1 $m = -2$ **3** $h = -2a$
2 $c = 3$ **4** $b = 3a$

447 The matrices **H, J, K** are of orders $p \times q$, $r \times s$ and $t \times r$ respectively.
DN Can the matrix products **HJK** and **KJH** both be formed ?

1 $p = t$ **3** $r = q$
2 $q = s$ **4** $s = p$

448 P is the point with parameter 2 on the rectangular hyperbola $x = 4t$,
DS $y = 4/t$ and the points Q,R on the curve have parameters q, r respectively.
The line through P perpendicular to QR meets the hyperbola again
at S. What is the numerical value of the parameter of S ?

1 $q + r = 5$ **2** $qr = 6$

449 Are the following equations consistent ?
DS

$$x + ay + b = 0$$
$$2x + cy + d = 0$$

1 $c = 2a$ **2** $d = 2b$

PAPER 45

450

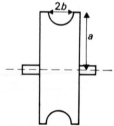

A pulley wheel is made from a cylindrical blank of radius a by cutting
in it a groove of semi-circular cross-section of radius b. What volume of
material is removed during this operation ?

A $\pi^2 ab^2$ **C** $\pi^2 b^2(a - \frac{3b}{8})$ **E** $\pi^2 b^2(a - \frac{4b}{3\pi})$

B $\pi^2 b^2(a - \frac{b}{2})$ **D** $\pi^2 b^2(a - \frac{2b}{\pi})$

451 The complementary function of the differential equation

$$\frac{d^2y}{dx^2} + 7\frac{dy}{dx} + 12y = 12x + 7$$

is of the form

A x

B $pe^{-3x} + qe^{-4x}$

C $pe^{-3x} + qe^{-4x} + x$

D $pe^{3x} + qe^{4x}$

E $pe^{3x} + qe^{4x} + x$

452 The number of rational roots of the equation

$$\begin{vmatrix} x^2 & (x+1)^2 \\ (x+1)^2 & (x+2)^2 \end{vmatrix} = 0 \text{ is}$$

A 4

B 3

C 2

D 1

E 0

453 How many points are common to the spiral $4\pi r = \theta$ ($\theta \geqslant 0$) and the circle $r = \cos \theta$?

A 3

B 4

C 5

D 6

E More than 6.

454

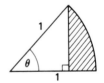

The diagram shows part of a unit circle. When θ is small, the shaded area is of order θ^n where n is

A 0

B 1

C 2

D 3

E more than 3

455

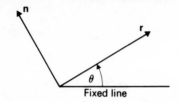

Fixed line

The perpendicular *unit* vectors **r** and **n** are rotating in their plane. $\dot{\textbf{n}}$, the derivative of **n** with respect to time, is

A $\dot{\theta}\textbf{r}$ **C** $\dot{\theta}$ **E** $-\dot{\theta}\textbf{n}$

B $-\dot{\theta}\textbf{r}$ **D** $\dot{\theta}\textbf{n}$

456 If $f(n) \equiv 3^{4n-2} + 5^{2n-1}$ where n is a positive integer then it can be deduced that $f(n+1) + 3f(n) \equiv 28(3^{4n-1} + 5^{2n-1})$.

The highest common factor of all the $f(r)$ is

A 56   **C** 14   **E** 1

B 28   **D** 7

457 If $k > 0$ is a necessary condition for the truth of proposition P then

MC

1 when $k = -1$, P is false

2 when P is false, k is negative

3 when $k = 0$, P may be true

458 A matrix **T** which has the property $\textbf{T}^2 = \textbf{T}$ is said to be *idempotent*.

MC If **P** and **Q** are 2×2 idempotent matrices then

1 the matrix **PQ** idempotent

2 $\textbf{P}^n = \textbf{P}$ for all positive integer n

3 if **Q** is non-singular then $|\textbf{Q}| = 1$

459 If z is a complex number such that $|z - \sqrt{2}| = 1$ then

MC

1 $|z| > \sqrt{2} - 1$

2 $|z| < \sqrt{2} + 1$

3 $-\frac{\pi}{4} \leqslant \arg z \leqslant \frac{\pi}{4}$

PAPER 46

460 a and b are real and non-zero.
RA
   1 $z^2 + az + b = 0$ has a complex root of unit modulus.
   2 $b = 1$

461 S_n denotes the sum of n terms of an arithmetic series.
RA
   1 $S_{p+q} = 0$ **2** $S_p = S_q$

462 $p(x)$ is a polynomial.
RA
   1 $y = p(x)$ has a point of inflexion at $x = a$.
   2 $(x - a)^2$ is a factor of $p(x)$.

463 **1** $x^2 + y^2 = 0$ **2** $\cos x = \cosh y$
RA

464 **1** The equations
RA
$$ax + by + c = 0$$
$$px + qy + r = 0$$
                                      are consistent.

   2 $\begin{vmatrix} a & b \\ p & q \end{vmatrix} = 0$

465 $p(x) = x^3 + ax^2 + bx + c$
DN
   How many real roots does the equation $p(x) = 0$ have ?

   1 $f(h) < 0$ **3** $h < 1$
   2 $f(h^2) > 0$ **4** $h > 0$

466 Find the numerical value of the determinant $\begin{vmatrix} p & 3 & 1 \\ 1 & r & 2 \\ s & 1 & q \end{vmatrix}$
DN

   1 $p = 1$ **3** $r = 3$
   2 $q = 2$ **4** $s = 4$

467 When evaluated, does $\int_0^{\frac{\pi}{2}} \cos^m \theta \sin^n \theta \, d\theta$, where m, n are positive
DS integers, contain a factor π ?

   1 m is odd.   **2** n is odd.

468
DS Are the equations
$$x + ay + b = 0$$
$$2x + cy + d = 0$$

consistent ?

1 $c \neq 2a$ **2** $d \neq 2b$

469
DS What are the numerical values of the co-ordinates of the centroid of the triangle whose vertices lie on the rectangular hyperbola $x = 4t$, $y = \dfrac{4}{t}$ and have parameters p, q, r ?

1 $p + q + r = 6$ **2** $qr + rp + pq = 11$

PAPER 47

470 Which of the points   **A** $(0, -1, 3)$,   **B** $(1, 1, -1)$,   **C** $(2, 3, 3)$, **D** $(2, 1, -2)$,   **E** $(2, -2, 0)$ is furthest from the plane $3x - y + 4z = 7$?

471 $\displaystyle\int \dfrac{dx}{\sqrt{(9 - 4x^2)}}$ is

A $-\frac{1}{2}\sqrt{9 - 4x^2} + c$ **C** $\frac{1}{2}\arcsin\dfrac{2x}{3} + c$ **E** $\frac{3}{2}\arcsin\dfrac{2x}{3} + c$

B $-\dfrac{1}{4x}\sqrt{9 - 4x^2} + c$ **D** $\frac{2}{3}\arcsin\dfrac{2x}{3} + c$

472 Which line, if any, is the first to contain an error ?

The equation $\dfrac{d^2y}{dx^2} - n^2y = 0$ is satisfied by

$y = ae^{nx}$	line 1
$y = b \cosh nx$	line 2
$y = c \sinh nx$	line 3

Hence its general solution,
$y = ae^{nx} + b \cosh nx - c \sinh nx$,
contains three arbitrary constants.

A   line 1   **C**   line 3   **E**   There is no error.
B   line 2   **D**   line 4

473 Two countries X, Y are at war and have respectively x, y aircraft at time t. Y destroys X's aircraft at a rate λy and X destroys Y's at a rate λx where λ is constant. Y is unable to replace destroyed aircraft, but X replaces her aircraft at a constant rate μ. If the total number of aircraft at time t is z, then the first order differential equation satisfied by z is

A $\dot{z} + \lambda z + \mu = 0$ **D** $\dot{z} - \lambda z - \mu = 0$
B $\dot{z} + \lambda z - \mu = 0$ **E** none of these
C $\dot{z} - \lambda z + \mu = 0$

474 Express $\sin iy$ in terms of $\sinh y$.

A $\sinh y$ **C** $i \sinh y$ **E** $i \sinh iy$
B $-\sinh y$ **D** $-i \sinh y$

475 If $I_n = \int \tan^n \theta \, d\theta$, which of the following expressions is used to obtain a reduction formula for I_n ?

A $I_n + I_{n-2}$ **C** $I_n + I_{n-1}$ **E** $I_{n+1} + I_n$
B $I_n - I_{n-2}$ **D** $I_n - I_{n-1}$

476 Sketch the curve given parametrically by
$$x = a \cos^3 t$$
$$y = a \sin^3 t.$$

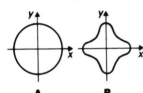

A   **B**   **C**   **D**   **E**

477 A curtain ring has external diameter $2(a + b)$ and internal diameter
MC $2(a - b)$. The expression for the ratio of its volume to its surface area contains a factor

1 π **2** a **3** b

478 The vectors
MC
$$a\mathbf{i} + \mathbf{j} + 2\mathbf{k}$$
$$\mathbf{i} + a\mathbf{j} + 2a\mathbf{k}$$
$$3\mathbf{i} - \mathbf{j} + \mathbf{k}$$

will NOT serve as basic vectors in three dimensions if a has the value

1   1   **2** -1 **3**   0

479 Two points P, Q are chosen from the set of points (±1, ±1, ±1) where
MC all possible sign combinations are taken. If the length of PQ = $2\sqrt{k}$,
k can be

1 1   **2** 2   **3** 3

Further Mathematics

Mechanics and Statistics

PAPER 48

480

G is the centroid of a non-uniform rod PQ of mass m. If its moment of inertia about an axis through P perpendicular to the rod is I, what is its moment of inertia about the parallel axis through Q ?

A $I + 9ma^2$ **C** $I + 3ma^2$

B $I + 5ma^2$ **D** $I + ma^2$

E It cannot be found without knowing how the mass is distributed.

481

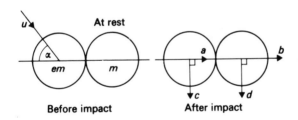

Before impact   After impact

The ratio of the masses of these impinging spheres is equal to e, the coefficient of restitution between them. How many of the velocity components a, b, c, d are independent of e ?

A 0   **C** 2   **E** 4

B 1   **D** 3

482 Pendulum 1 has length l and makes n_1 small oscillations per second. Pendulum 2 has length $4l$ and makes n_2 small oscillations per second.

$n_1 : n_2 =$

A $4:1$ **C** $2:1$ **E** $1:1$

B $1:4$ **D** $1:2$

483 The force **F** is represented in magnitude and direction by the vector $2\mathbf{i} - 2\mathbf{j} + \mathbf{k}$. The component of **F** in the direction of the vector $4\mathbf{i} + 3\mathbf{j}$ has magnitude

A $\frac{2}{5}$ **C** 2 **E** 3

B $\frac{2}{3}$ **D** $2\frac{4}{5}$

484 A rigid body of mass M is rotating about a fixed axis with angular speed ω and has radius of gyration k about the axis. The distance between this axis and a parallel one through the centre of mass is h. The moment of momentum of the body about the fixed axis is

A $\frac{1}{2}M(k^2 + h^2)\omega^2$ **C** $M(k^2 + h^2)\omega$ **E** none of these

B $\frac{1}{2}Mk^2\omega^2$ **D** $M(k^2 - h^2)\omega$

485
MC

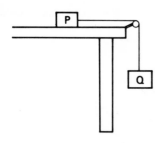

P has mass m and Q has mass λm. The coefficient of friction, μ, between P and the table is insufficient to prevent motion. The direction of the acceleration of Q relative to P is independent of

1 m **2** λ **3** μ

486
MC

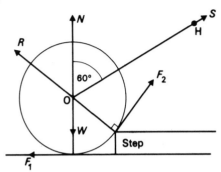

A gradually increasing force S is applied in the direction OH to the handle H of the roller until the force N just becomes zero. When this happens

1 $F_1 = 0$ **2** $F_2 = 0$ **3** $S = 2W$

487 Two particles of equal mass are moving on a smooth horizontal table
MC and are connected by a light straight spring. Which of the following will necessarily stay the same until the particles collide ?

1 The position of the centre of the spring.
2 The angular velocity of the spring.
3 The vector sum of the velocities of the particles.

488
MC

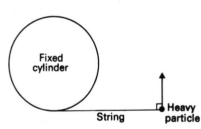

The particle and string are in contact with a smooth horizontal table. During the motion the string wraps itself on to the cylinder. Which of the following increase with time ?

1 The speed of the particle.
2 The angular speed of the straight part of the string.
3 The tension in the string.

489 The binomial distribution
MC
  1 can be applied to sampling, with replacement, from a finite population
  2 is always symmetrical about its mean
  3 has equal mean and variance

PAPER 49

490 A force acts along PQ.
RA
  1 Its vector moments about R and S are equal.
  2 P, Q, R, S are coplanar.

491
RA

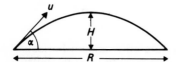

H is the greatest height of the projectile and R is its horizontal range.

  1 $H = \dfrac{u^2}{4g}$ **2** $R = \dfrac{u^2}{2g}$

492 The configuration of a conservative system is determined by a parameter
RA θ and the potential energy of the system is $V(\theta)$.

  1 $\theta = \alpha$ gives a position of unstable equilibrium of the system.

  2 $\dfrac{d^2V}{d\theta^2} > 0$ at $\theta = \alpha$.

493 A body of mass m kg is moving in a straight line, its motion being
DN resisted by a force proportional to its velocity. Find the numerical value of the time (in s) taken to reduce the velocity from u ms^{-1} to v ms^{-1}.

  1 When the velocity is 6 ms^{-1} the force is 3 N.
  2 $u = 8$ **3** $u = 2v$ **4** $m = 0 \cdot 5$

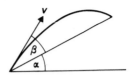

Find the numerical value of the time taken by the projectile to attain its greatest distance from the inclined plane.

1 $\alpha = 30°$ **3** $v \cos\beta = 30 \text{ ms}^{-1}$
2 $v \sin\beta = 40 \text{ ms}^{-1}$ **4** $g = 10 \text{ ms}^{-2}$

495 A particle performing SHM about O is instantaneously at a point P.
DN What is the distance OP ?

   1 The particle was last at P t seconds ago.
   2 It will return to P in $3t$ seconds.
   3 The period of the motion is 12 seconds.
   4 The amplitude of the motion is $0 \cdot 5$ metres.

496 A smooth cone of semi-vertical angle α is fixed with its axis vertical
DS and its vertex downwards. A particle of mass m is moving with speed
   v in a horizontal circle on the inner surface of the cone. Given that
   $g = 10 \text{ ms}^{-2}$, find the numerical value of the height (in cm) of the plane
   of the circle above the vertex of the cone.

   1 $\alpha = 30°$ **2** $v = 25 \text{ cms}^{-1}$

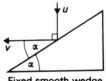

Fixed smooth wedge

What is the numerical value of the coefficient of restitution in this impact ?

1 $\tan \alpha = \frac{1}{2}$ **2** $2v = u$

498 A particle performs simple harmonic motion.
DS What is the amplitude of the oscillations ?

    1 The maximum speed attained is 3 ms^{-1}.
    2 The maximum acceleration attained is 18 ms^{-2}.

499 X is distributed normally. Find its standard deviation.
DS (Assume that statistical tables are available.)

    1 $P(X > 0) = \frac{1}{2}$ **2** $P(X > 1) = \frac{1}{4}$

PAPER 50

500

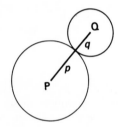

The circle centre P is fixed and the circle centre Q rolls on it without slipping. If PQ rotates at rate ω, at what rate does the circle centre Q rotate ?

A ω **C** $\dfrac{q\,\omega}{p}$ **E** $\dfrac{(p+q)\,\omega}{p}$

B $\dfrac{p\,\omega}{q}$ **D** $\dfrac{(p+q)\,\omega}{q}$

501 At time t a particle is at a distance x measured from the centre of the earth and is falling towards it under the action of a gravitational attraction inversely proportional to x^2 and a resistance proportional to the speed. h and k being positive constants, the form of the differential equation of the motion is

A $\ddot{x} + h\dot{x} + \dfrac{k}{x^2} = 0$

B $\ddot{x} + h\dot{x} - \dfrac{k}{x^2} = 0$

C $\ddot{x} - h\dot{x} + \dfrac{k}{x^2} = 0$

D $\ddot{x} - h\dot{x} - \dfrac{k}{x^2} = 0$

E impossible to determine without more information

502 Sphere P has twice the radius and twice the (uniform) density of sphere Q. The moment of inertia of P about a diameter is n times that of Q where n is

A 4   **B** 8   **C** 16   **D** 32   **E** 64

503 A particle moves on the spiral $r = a\,e^{\theta}$ so that the radius vector rotates at constant rate α. Find the radial component of its acceleration.

A r **C** $(1 - \alpha^2)r$ **E** 0
B $\alpha^2 r$ **D** $2\alpha^2 r$

504 A machine produces articles each of which has a probability p of being defective. The articles are packed four to a box. What is the probability that half of the articles in a box are defective ?

A p^2 **C** $p^2(1 - p)^2$ **E** $12p^2(1 - p)^2$
B $6p^2$ **D** $6p^2(1 - p)^2$

505
MC

The masses are connected by a taut inextensible string of length l and rest on a smooth horizontal table. m is given a horizontal velocity u at right-angles to the string. The time taken by the string to turn through a right angle will be independent of

1 m **2** M **3** l

506 If the position of a particle of mass m which is moving in a plane is given
MC by polar co-ordinates (r, θ) then

  1 the kinetic energy of the particle is $\frac{1}{2}m(\dot{r}^2 + r \dot{\theta}^2)$
  2 its linear momentum has magnitude $m(\dot{r} + r \dot{\theta})$
  3 its moment of momentum about the pole has magnitude $mr^2 \dot{\theta}$

507
MC

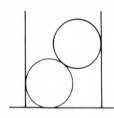

The diagram shows a smooth heavy cylindrical tube containing two heavy spheres at rest on a rough horizontal table. It can be deduced that

  1 in equilibrium the forces which the tube exerts on the system of two spheres form a couple
  2 in equilibrium the forces which the table exerts on the tube reduce to a couple
  3 the position is certainly one of equilibrium.

508 The theorem of perpendicular axes
MC
  1 is applicable to laminas but not to solid bodies
  2 when expressed in terms of radii of gyration takes the form $p^2+q^2=r^2$ where p, q, r are lengths
  3 makes reference to the centre of mass of the body

509 A distribution with mean 3 and variance 5 CANNOT be
MC
  1 binomial   **2** Poisson   **3** normal

PAPER 51

510 A particle falling vertically strikes a smooth fixed inclined plane of angle
RA α and rebounds horizontally. The coefficient of restitution between the two bodies is e.

  1 $e = \frac{1}{3}$ **2** $\tan \alpha = \frac{1}{3}$

511 A rigid body with centroid G is rotating freely under gravity about a
RA fixed axis.

  1 Its moment of momentum about the axis is conserved.
  2 The axis passes through G.

512 $P(x)$ is a discrete probability function.
RA
  1 $P(x)$ has a binomial distribution.
  2 The mean and variance of $P(x)$ are equal.

513 A compound pendulum has mass M and moment of inertia I about an
DN axis through its centroid. It makes small oscillations about a parallel
axis at a distance h from the first. Find the numerical value of the period
of oscillation in seconds.

  1 $I = 3 \text{ kg m}^2$ **3** $g = 10 \text{ ms}^{-2}$
  2 $M = 1 \cdot 5 \text{ kg}$ **4** $h = 0 \cdot 2 \text{m}$

514
DN

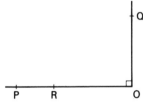

A ball thrown from P strikes a vertical wall at Q and rebounds to R.
Find the coefficient of restitution between the ball and the wall.

  1 OP $= 20 \text{ m}$ **3** OR $= 15 \text{ m}$
  2 OQ $= 15 \text{ m}$ **4** The ball strikes the wall horizontally.

515 A particle is moving with SHM of amplitude a cm and period T seconds.
DN P, Q are points on its path where its distances from the centre of the
motion are p cm and q cm respectively. The centre of oscillation lies
between P and Q. Find the numerical value of the time which it takes
to move directly from P to Q.

  1 $a = 4$ **3** $p = 2$
  2 $T = \pi$ **4** $p^2 + q^2 = 16$

516 The bob of a freely suspended simple pendulum of length l is given a
DS horizontal velocity u. Will the string go slack ?

  1 $u^2 > 4gl$ **2** $u^2 < 5gl$

517 A shell fired out to sea from the top of a cliff 50 metres high with initial
DS components of velocity u ms^{-1} horizontally and v ms^{-1} vertically
upwards, hits the water 300 metres from the foot of the cliff. Given
$g = 9 \cdot 8$ ms^{-2} what is the numerical value of the time of flight ?

  1 $u = 30$ **2** $v = 44$

518
DS P is the highest point of a vertical circle of radius a metres and a smooth straight wire joins it to another point Q of the circle. PQ is inclined at θ to the horizontal. Given $g = 9 \cdot 8$ ms^{-2}, find the time taken by a bead to slide from P to Q.

1 $a = 0 \cdot 5$ **2** $\theta = 20°$

519
DS A simple pendulum has mass M and length l. Taking g to be 10 ms^{-2}, what is the numerical value of the period of oscillation in seconds ?

1 $M = 0 \cdot 3$ kg   **2** $l = 2$ metres

PAPER 52

520 The force **F** is represented in magnitude and direction by the vector $4\mathbf{i} - 3\mathbf{j}$ and acts through the point with position vector $2\mathbf{i} + \mathbf{j}$. The moment of **F** about the origin has magnitude

A 2   **C** $5\sqrt{5}$ **E** 11
B 5   **D** 10

521 A rigid body oscillates as a compound pendulum about a smooth horizontal axis and has radius of gyration k about the axis. The distance between this axis and a parallel one through the centre of mass is h. The length of the simple equivalent pendulum is

A $\dfrac{k^2}{gh}$ **C** $\dfrac{k^2 - h^2}{h}$ **E** $\dfrac{k^2}{h}$

B $\dfrac{gh}{k^2}$ **D** $\dfrac{k^2 + h^2}{h}$

522 A car is accelerating forwards along a horizontal road under the action of its engine which drives its rear wheels. What are the directions of the frictional forces from the road acting on the tyres ?

	Front	*Rear*
A	Forwards	Forwards
B	Backwards	Forwards
C	Forwards	Backwards
D	Backwards	Backwards
E	There is no friction.	Forwards

523

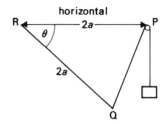

QR is a uniform rod of mass m, smoothly hinged to a fixed point R. A string tied to Q passes over a smooth peg P and carries a mass M at its other end. PR = QR = $2a$. If the potential energy of the system is $V(\theta)$ then the value of $\dfrac{1}{ag}\dfrac{dV}{d\theta}$ is

A $\quad -m\sin\theta + 4M\sin\dfrac{\theta}{2}$

B $\quad -m\cos\theta - 2M\cos\dfrac{\theta}{2}$

C $\quad -m\cos\theta + 2M\cos\dfrac{\theta}{2}$

D $\quad m\cos\theta - 2M\cos\dfrac{\theta}{2}$

E $\quad m\cos\theta + 2M\cos\dfrac{\theta}{2}$

524 A continuous distribution function $p(x)$ has mean 2 and variance 5. What is the value of $\int_{-\infty}^{\infty} x^2 p(x)\,dx$?

A 1	**C** 9	**E** 29
B 7	**D** 21	

525
MC A smooth straight tube is made to rotate in a horizontal plane with constant angular velocity ω. A particle in the tube at a distance r from the axis of rotation is acted on by a horizontal force F from the tube. Without using the equation of the radial motion, an expression for F can be obtained in which F is proportional to

1 r $\qquad\qquad$ **2** $\dot{r}$ $\qquad\qquad$ **3** ω

526
MC In a test, a stationary shell, exploded above a plain, breaks into two fragments of equal mass.

1 The fragments have the same initial velocity.
2 The two trajectories are parts of the same parabola.
3 For given energy of explosion, if the separation of the fragments when they land is a maximum, the fragments will hit the ground at 45°.

527
MC

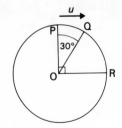

A particle resting on top of a smooth fixed sphere centre O is given a horizontal velocity u which may be chosen so that the particle leaves the sphere at

1 P   **2** Q   **3** R

528 A uniform rod PQ with centre G and mass $6m$ is replaced by masses
MC m at P and Q, and $4m$ at G. This replacement leaves unchanged the moment of inertia about

  1 an axis perpendicular to PQ and passing through G
  2 an axis perpendicular to PQ and passing through P
  3 any axis perpendicular to PQ

529 To estimate the proportion of adults in a population who are over 2m
MC tall, making use of normal distribution tables, it is necessary to know

  1 the mean height of an adult
  2 the variance of the heights of adults
  3 the number of adults in the population

PAPER 53

530 **P, Q, R, S, T, U** are non-coplanar forces.
RA
  1 They are in equilibrium.
  2 They can be represented completely by the sides of a tetrahedron.

531 A uniform lamina is rotating about a fixed axis. At time t its angular
RA speed is ω radians per second, its angular momentum is a kg m²s⁻¹ and its kinetic energy is k joules.

  1 $a = k$ **2** $\omega = 2$

Answers

Papers	0	1	2	3	4	5	6	7	8	9
1	C	D	B	D	B	B	C	E	C	A
2	B	A	B	E	A	A	D	D	C	D
3	A	B	C	E	A	B	E	D	C	A
4	D	A	C	E	B	E	B	C	D	B
5	C	B	E	A	D	D	C	A	A	E
6	C	C	A	E	B	C	C	D	A	A
7	A	E	A	C	D	A	A	C	A	B
8	B	B	E	C	D	B	E	A	E	B
9	A	A	B	C	E	D	A	C	D	E
10	D	B	A	D	E	C	A	D	C	C
11	E	C	D	A	C	C	E	B	C	E
12	D	D	B	C	E	E	C	E	C	D
13	B	D	E	C	A	D	E	A	B	A
14	A	C	C	D	E	A	D	B	E	B
15	A	B	B	B	C	A	A	D	A	B
16	E	B	B	C	E	D	C	A	E	A
17	D	E	A	D	D	E	A	E	B	C
18	E	A	D	D	A	A	E	E	B	E
19	B	E	C	E	C	A	D	B	C	B
20	D	A	A	A	E	B	D	D	B	B
21	D	C	A	C	D	B	D	D	A	B
22	D	A	E	D	A	B	D	B	C	D
23	D	C	A	A	E	C	E	D	D	B
24	B	C	C	D	E	D	E	D	C	E
25	C	E	B	E	B	B	C	D	B	C
26	B	C	B	A	B	E	E	D	D	C
27	E	E	C	C	D	E	B	A	A	E
28	D	C	E	C	D	A	A	C	B	A
29	A	D	E	D	D	C	C	B	E	C
30	B	A	A	D	B	A	A	C	A	A
	0	1	2	3	4	5	6	7	8	9

Papers	0	1	2	3	4	5	6	7	8	9
31	E	D	B	E	A	B	C	B	B	A
32	E	A	E	E	C	D	A	C	B	A
33	C	E	B	D	B	B	A	D	A	E
34	B	A	C	D	A	C	C	B	D	A
35	D	A	D	C	A	C	D	B	D	D
36	D	E	B	A	D	A	C	C	A	E
37	B	D	B	D	C	E	A	C	A	C
38	E	C	D	B	C	D	D	A	E	A
39	C	E	E	B	E	C	D	B	D	A
40	B	D	A	A	D	C	C	A	A	A
41	E	C	C	A	A	E	D	C	A	A
42	A	A	B	D	B	C	D	E	B	C
43	C	D	B	D	E	C	E	C	E	E
44	E	B	C	C	D	C	B	B	C	C
45	E	B	E	D	D	B	C	D	C	E
46	A	A	E	A	E	E	B	A	B	E
47	D	C	D	B	C	A	C	E	B	A
48	C	D	C	A	E	A	B	E	C	D
49	A	D	D	B	C	C	C	A	D	D
50	E	A	E	E	D	B	E	D	B	B
51	D	B	D	E	B	C	D	A	B	C
52	D	E	B	C	C	C	C	B	A	B
53	D	C	B	A	D	B	A	C	C	A
54	B	E	A	E	C	C	B	A	A	B
55	A	B	B	C	E	C	A	D	A	D
56	A	B	C	E	C	D	B	B	E	B
	0	1	2	3	4	5	6	7	8	9

Multiple Choice Questions on Advanced Level Mathematics
Copyright © 1975 G. Bell & Sons Ltd

532 **1** The probability of just one success in two (Bernoulli) trials is $\frac{4}{9}$
RA **2** The probability of success in a single trial is $\frac{1}{3}$

533 A body is accelerating in a straight line under the action of a force
DN proportional to the square of its velocity. Find the numerical value of the
distance which it covers while its velocity increases from u ms^{-1} to
v ms^{-1}.

1 $u = 4$
2 $v = 3u$
3 When the velocity is 6 ms^{-1} the force is 36 N.
4 The mass of the body is 2 kg.

534 Two particles are simultaneously
DN projected in a vertical plane as
shown. What is the direction of the
line joining the particles t seconds
later ?

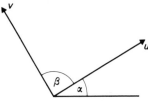

1 $\alpha = 30°$ **3** $u = v$
2 $\beta = 90°$ **4** $t = 2$

535 A flywheel, spinning with angular speed ω about its centre of mass,
DN is brought to rest by a frictional couple. Find ω .

1 The magnitude of the couple is constant.
2 The moment of inertia is given.
3 The time taken is given.
4 The angle turned through is given.

536 Does the equation $\ddot{x} = a\dot{x} + bx$ represent damped harmonic motion ?
DS
    1 $a > 0$ **2** $b > 0$

537 A simple pendulum of length 1·4 metres is making small oscillations
DS in a railway carriage which is accelerating horizontally. Calculate the
time of swing given $g = 9·8$ ms^{-2}.

1 The plane of oscillation is parallel to the rails.
2 The acceleration of the train is 3 ms^{-2}.

538 A particle performs S.H.M. about the point O. P is one extreme of the
DS motion and M is the mid-point of OP. How long does the particle take
to move directly from M to P ?

1 The amplitude is 10 cm.
2 The period of the motion is 3 s.

539 A random variable X has a Poisson distribution. Find $P(X = 2)$.
DS

    1 $P(X = 0) = e^{-1}$ **2** The mean is 1.

PAPER 54

540 Two waves are represented by $x_1 = 4 \cos \omega t$ and $x_2 = 3 \cos(\omega t + \frac{\pi}{2})$.
The wave represented by $x_1 + x_2$ has amplitude

    A 1   **C** 7   **E** 25
    B 5   **D** 10

541

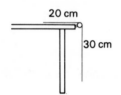

The uniform flexible cord, which is in limiting equilibrium, passes over a smooth light pulley at the corner of the table. Find the coefficient of friction between it and the table.

    A $\frac{2}{5}$ **B** $\frac{3}{5}$ **C** $\frac{2}{3}$ **D** 1   **E** $\frac{3}{2}$

542 In an experiment a ball-bearing of mass m falls from the rest through a vertical tube of length l, full of syrup. The resisting force is kv^2 per unit mass, where $v = \dot{x}$ and x is the height of the ball-bearing above the bottom of the tube at time t. Find the first order differential equation of the motion in a form involving $\dfrac{dv}{dx}$.

    A $v\dfrac{dv}{dx} = kv^2 - g$ **D** $v\dfrac{dv}{dx} = kv^2 + g$

    B $v\dfrac{dv}{dx} = g - kv^2$ **E** $\dfrac{dv}{dx} = kv^2 - g$

    C $mv\dfrac{dv}{dx} = kv^2 - mg$

543 A heavy bead is moving on a rough circular wire which is fixed in a vertical plane. The coefficient of friction between the two is μ. In the position shown find $\dot\theta \dfrac{d\dot\theta}{d\theta}$

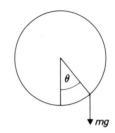

A $-g \sin\theta - \mu g \cos\theta - \mu\,\dot\theta^2 r$
B $-g \sin\theta - \mu g \cos\theta$
C $-g \sin\theta + \mu g \cos\theta - \mu\,\dot\theta^2 r$
D $-g \sin\theta - \mu\,\dot\theta^2 r$
E More information is needed.

544 An arbitrary point of a uniform rod of unit length is at a distance x from one end. The root mean square value of x is

A $\dfrac{1}{2}$ **C** $\dfrac{\sqrt3}{3}$ **E** none of these

B $\dfrac{\sqrt3}{6}$ **D** $\dfrac{2\sqrt3}{3}$

545 A particle moves with constant acceleration in a straight line.
MC Which of the following graphs of its motion are parabolic ?

   1 The v,t graph   **2** The s,t graph   **3** The v,s graph

546 The diagram shows a smooth
MC semicircular wire fixed in a vertical plane. If small beads P, Q are simultaneously gently displaced from the top to move in opposite directions, P being threaded on the wire and Q sliding down its outside, then

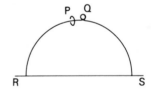

   1 when Q leaves the wire, P has acceleration g downwards
   2 P and Q have the same speed when they reach the horizontal RS
   3 P and Q reach RS simultaneously

547
MC

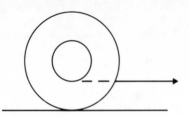

The spool is resting on a rough horizontal table. When a small force is applied to the thread

1 the spool moves to the right
2 the thread is wound on to the spool
3 the spool rotates clockwise

548
MC

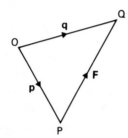

A force **F** is completely represented by $\overline{PQ}$. P, Q have position vectors **p**, **q**. The magnitude of its moment about O is

1 $2\triangle OPQ$ **2** $|\,\mathbf{p} \times \mathbf{F}\,|$ **3** $|\,\mathbf{q} \times \mathbf{F}\,|$

549
MC An expression of the form $(p^2 + q^2)^{\frac{1}{2}}$ may be used to calculate

1 the hypotenuse of a triangle knowing the other two sides
2 the radius of gyration of a body about an axis knowing its radius of gyration about the parallel axis through the centre of mass and the distance between the axes
3 the standard deviation of a distribution knowing its standard deviation about a working mean and the difference between the true and working means.

Harder Questions

550
MC

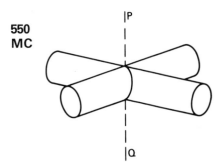

The axes of two equal circular cylinders intersect at right angles. A cross-section of their common volume could be

1 a circle　　　　**2** an ellipse　　　　**3** a square

551 A unit cube can be cut by a plane so that the section is
MC
  1 an equilateral triangle with any given perimeter up to $3\sqrt{2}$
  2 a regular hexagon with perimeter $3\sqrt{2}$
  3 a rectangle with any given perimeter up to $2 + 2\sqrt{2}$

552 A cylindrical hole of length l cm is bored diametrically through a sphere
DS of radius r cm. What is the numerical value of the volume remaining ?

  1 $l = 10$　　　　　　　　**2** $r = 15$

553 Let :
MC $s(n)$ denote the number of distinct segments into which n points divide a line,

  $r(n)$ denote the maximum number of distinct regions into which n lines can divide a plane,

  $R(n)$ denote the maximum number of distinct regions into which n planes can divide space,

  then

  1 $s(n) = n$
  2 $r(n) = r(n - 1) + s(n - 1)$
  3 $R(n) = R(n - 1) + r(n - 1)$

554 The number of different ways of arranging 4 points in a plane so that there are precisely two different values for the distance between any pair of them is

A 2   **C** 4   **E** 6
B 3   **D** 5

555 Some of the n airports in a country are interconnected by direct
MC passenger flights. If from any airport P there are f_p direct flights, then

    1 the product of all the f_p is even
    2 there must be two airports, R,S say, for which $f_r = f_s$
    3 the sum of all the f_p is even

556 If in a certain country there are six major cities, each pair of which are
MC the termini *either* of a stopping train service *or* of a non-stop inter-city service, then

    1 the total number of inter-city journeys which are available must be even
    2 from each city there are either at least three stopping services or at least three inter-city services
    3 there are three cities which are linked by services of the same type

557 If m and n are integers and $7m + n$ is a perfect square then n can be
MC
    1   4   **2**   5   **3**   6

558 **1** n is a prime number greater than 3.
RA **2** $n^2 - 1$ is a multiple of 24.

559 All of the balls in a bag are either black or white. How many are there ?
DS
    1 The probability that a single ball drawn at random is black is $\frac{7}{13}$ of the probability that it is white.
    2 The (non-zero) probability that two balls simultaneously drawn at random are both black is $\frac{7}{26}$ of the probability that they are both white.

560 Is $(x - 1)(x + 3)$ a factor of $(x^2 + ax + b)(x^2 + bx + a)$?
DS
    1 $a = 1$ **2** $b = -6$

561 For $n = 0, 1, 2, \ldots$
MC
      let $u_n = v_{n+1} - v_n$
      and $v_n = u_{n+1} - u_n$

then for $n = 0, 1, 2, \ldots$

1 $u_{n+2} = 2u_{n+1}$
2 $v_1, v_2, v_3, \ldots \ldots$ is a GP with common ratio 2.
3 $u_n = v_n$

562
DS
In the sequence $u_0, u_1, u_2, \ldots, u_0 = a \ (\neq 0)$ and $u_1 = b$.

For all $n \geqslant 0$, $u_n u_{n+2} = u_{n+1} + 1$.

What is the numerical value of u_6 ?

1 $a = 3$ **2** $b = 4$

563 The number of values of x which satisfy the equation

$$\begin{vmatrix} x^2 & (x-1)^2 & (x-2)^2 \\ (x+1)^2 & x^2 & (x-1)^2 \\ (x+2)^2 & (x+1)^2 & x^2 \end{vmatrix} = 8 \text{ is}$$

A 0   **C** 4   **E** infinite
B 2   **D** 6

564
RA
a, b, c are non-negative.
1 $a^3 + b^3 + c^3 = 3abc$
2 $a^2 + b^2 + c^2 = bc + ca + ab$

565

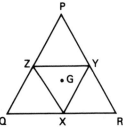

PQR is a uniform equilateral triangular lamina, XYZ are the mid-points of its sides and G is its centroid. If I is its moment of inertia about the axis perpendicular to its plane through G, what is the moment of inertia of PZY about this axis ?

A $\dfrac{I}{6}$ **C** $\dfrac{7I}{24}$ **E** $\dfrac{31I}{96}$

B $\dfrac{I}{4}$ **D** $\dfrac{5I}{16}$

If P is a point on the circumference of the circle S with centre C which rolls with uniform angular velocity on a fixed circle of twice its radius then

1 the locus of P is a diameter of the fixed circle
2 the motion of P is simple harmonic
3 S makes two revolutions before it returns to its starting position

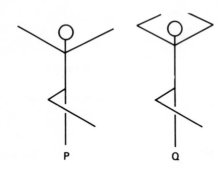

A skater is spinning about a vertical axis and has her arms extended as in P. On changing to the position Q, which does not alter the position of her centre of gravity,

1 her moment of inertia about the axis is decreased
2 her angular velocity is increased
3 her kinetic energy is unchanged

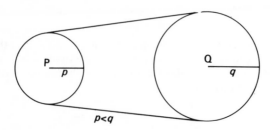

$p < q$

Flywheels P and Q can rotate freely on fixed axles. P is spinning and Q is at rest. If the belt suddenly tightens without slipping, then

1 the KE of the system is conserved

2 the moment of momentum of the system about the centre of P is conserved

3 the final angular velocity of Q is smaller than that of P

569
MC

The diagram shows two small smooth beads each of mass m which have been simultaneously gently displaced from the top of a circular wire of mass M on which they are threaded. The wire stands vertically on a horizontal table.

1 If the wire rises from the table when $\theta = \alpha$ then $\arccos \frac{2}{3} < \alpha < \frac{\pi}{2}$

2 If $m = 3M$ the wire will rise.

3 If $m = 2M$ the wire will not rise.

Notes On Solutions

51 $\cos 2\alpha = (\cos \alpha - \sin\alpha)(\cos \alpha + \sin \alpha)$

114 Note the symmetry about $y = x - 1$.

117 Use the intersecting chord property.

118 Reduce all of the y co-ordinates by a.

134 If $T = \tan \frac{\theta}{2}$ then $2 \Rightarrow \frac{2T}{1+T^2} = \frac{2t}{1+t^2} \Leftrightarrow (T-t)(1-Tt) = 0$ so that $t = \tan \frac{\theta}{2}$ or $\cot \frac{\theta}{2}$.

152 If $P = 6$, $R = 31$, and if $P = n$, $R = 1 + {}^nC_2 + {}^nC_4$. This expression is $1 +$ (number of chords) $+$ (number of points within the circle at which chords intersect). Investigate why R is of this form.

159 If there is a solution in the third quadrant then $k < 0$ and there can be no solution in the first. If there is a solution in the fourth quadrant k may be either positive or negative and so there may or may not be a solution in the first quadrant.

163 For $x = -2$ the functions are not real.

165 There are eight possible combinations of the signs of the factors $x - 1$, $y + 2, y - 2x - 1$, yet the lines divide the plane into only seven regions. Why is this ?

169 Square the expression.

174 **1** is the condition that lengths p, q, r can form a right-angled triangle with hypotenuse r. **2** is the condition that the length r is equal to the sum of the other two. These conditions cannot be satisfied simultaneously.

175 **1** $\Rightarrow n = 2$ or 4, **2** $\Rightarrow n = 2$ or 3.

180 The modulus is $2|\cos \theta|$.

193 If $PH - PK = 2$ the locus of P is that part of the x-axis for which $x \leqslant -1$.

214 The x-axis is an asymptote of $y = \dfrac{1}{p(x)}$.

215 In **1**, x can take all values less than or equal to 1 whereas in **2**, x cannot be less than -1.

217 Put $x = at^2, y = 2at$ in the equation of the chord.

239 Consider the intersection of the line with the axes.

240 $\displaystyle\int_0^{\frac{\pi}{2}} \cos x \, dx = \int_0^{\frac{\pi}{2}} \sin x \, dx.$ $\sin^3 x < \sin^2 x < \sin x$ for $0 < x < \frac{\pi}{2}$.

243 As $x \to 3$, $f(x) \to 1\cdot 2$ but $f(x)$ is not defined for $x = 3$.
If $f(x)$ is to be continuous at $x = 3$, then $f(3)$ must be separately defined to be $1\cdot 2$.

244 $^{500}C_{250}\,(\tfrac{1}{2})^{500} \approx 0\cdot 036$

249 The general solution is $2n\pi \pm \dfrac{\pi}{3}$.

253 Consider $y = \ln x$ to show **1** $\not\Rightarrow$ **2** and $y = e^x$ to show **2** $\not\Rightarrow$ **1**.

258 The length of PR is $y\,\dfrac{dy}{dx}$ which equals $\dfrac{a}{2}$

304 The minimum length of the third side is when it is perpendicular to the side representing the total reaction from the plane.

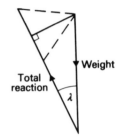

316 The question is equivalent to asking " Is the centre of mass at the centre of the base of the hemisphere ? " **3** is irrelevant so the key is seen to be **C** without doing any working out.

321 Because the gun recoils, the angle of elevation of the shell will exceed α. To see that it decreases with M consider the effect of letting M become large.

324 The direction of the smoke trail is that of the wind relative to the ship.

326 There is no relative acceleration.

329 The centres of gravity of the two semicircles are collinear with P. The centre of gravity of the shaded part will lie on this line and the angle will be independent of g, a and k.

332 From the triangle of velocities it can be seen that **2** $\Rightarrow u > v > \dfrac{u}{2}$.

341 As there is no horizontal force on the system its centroid falls vertically.

348 Cf. **288**.

357 As the diagonals of a rectangle are of equal length, OM = half the length of the rod.

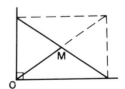

373 $f(1)$ has not been examined.

392 The equation represents one sphere.

399 The result also applies in the case $n > m > 0$.

410 The third one is either $\dfrac{\sqrt{11}}{4}$ or $-\dfrac{\sqrt{11}}{4}$.

412 Had the question been " Given only that all questions in this book were composed either by Payne or by Pennycuick and that all the latter's questions are sound, by whom was this question composed ? " there would have been insufficient information to answer it and so it would have been an unsound question. Thus it would have been composed by Payne and the information would have been sufficient, making the above reasoning invalid ! This is an example of Russell's paradox, perhaps the best known case of which is " All Cretans are liars ".

418 $x - a$ is a factor of $x^3 - px + q$ and its derivative. Use the sum of the roots for **3**.

424 If your answer was wrong, try lettering $\triangle$PQR in the opposite cyclic order.

430 If $\mathbf{X} \neq \mathbf{I}$ or $-\mathbf{I}$, the most general form of $\mathbf{X}$ is $\begin{bmatrix} 0 & x \\ x^{-1} & 0 \end{bmatrix}$ where $x \neq 0$.

436 If N is a perfect square the answer is **D**, otherwise it is **B**.

438 If P is false, k could be zero.

445 There is an asymptote parallel to the x-axis unless the degree of $p(x)$ exceeds that of $q(x)$.

456 $f(1) = 14$

461 $\mathbf{1} \Rightarrow 2a + (p + q - 1)d = 0$, $\quad \mathbf{2} \Rightarrow (p - q)\,[2a + (p + q - 1)d] = 0$ $\quad$ so that **2** does not necessarily imply **1**.

508 Which of the statements are correct for the theorem of parallel axes ?

530 If **2** is true, one and only one force has moment about a side of the tetrahedron, denying **1**.

543 **A** is correct when $\dot{\theta} > 0$ and **C** when $\dot{\theta} < 0$.

546 After Q leaves the wire the downward acceleration of P is less than g so **3** is false.

550 Take, for **1**, the plane through PQ and one of the axes ; for **2**, the plane through PQ bisecting the angle between the axes ; and for **3**, a plane perpendicular to PQ.

551

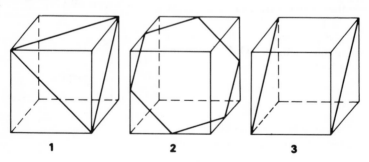

| 1 | 2 | 3 |

1 shows the equilateral triangular section of maximum perimeter. Any smaller perimeter can be obtained by choosing a suitable plane parallel to that shown.

2 shows the regular hexagonal section.

3 The greatest perimeter is $2 + 2\sqrt{2}$ but all rectangular sections have perimeter greater than 2.

552 $V = \dfrac{\pi l^3}{6}$

554

4 vertices of a regular pentagon

555 **1** Consider just two airports to show that this is not necessarily true.

2 If there are k airports which operate direct passenger flights, then, for each of them, $0 < f < k$ so that there are only $k - 1$ possible values of f and two of the k airports will have to have the same value of f.

3 Each flight can be paired with the return one.

556 **1** Two journeys, one in each direction, can be made on each inter-city route.

2 Five routes leave each city. $2 + 2 < 5$.

3 Suppose that at least three inter-city services leave P, going to Q, R. S. Assuming the services between Q and R and between R and S are stopping, the service between Q and S will either complete the triangle PQR or the triangle QRS. It makes no difference if three stopping services leave P.

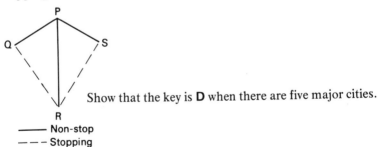

Show that the key is **D** when there are five major cities.

——— Non-stop
— — — Stopping

557   Consider the squares of numbers of the forms $7m \pm 1$, $7m \pm 2$, $7m \pm 3$.

121

558 Of the consecutive numbers $n-1$, n, $n+1$, one is a multiple of 3. Given **1**, it is either $n-1$ or $n+1$. Since these are consecutive even numbers, one is a multiple of 4. Thus **1** $\Rightarrow$ **2**.

Given **2**, $(n-1)(n+1)$ is a multiple of 24. This is so when $n-1=24$ and n is composite.

559 **1** $\Rightarrow 7w = 13b$

2 $\Rightarrow 7w(w-1) = 26b(b-1)$

Solutions of the second equation are $w=13$, $b=7$, and $w=40$, $b=21$. **1** is needed in order to make the answer unique.

561 **3** is necessarily true for all n other than $n=0$.

563 $r_1 = r_1 - 2r_2 + r_3$ is a useful first step.

564 $a^3 + b^3 + c^3 - 3abc = (a+b+c)(a^2+b^2+c^2-bc-ca-ab)$.

Since a, b, c are non-negative, $a+b+c=0 \Rightarrow a=b=c=0$.

565 Triangle XYZ also has centroid G and its moment of inertia about the axis is $I/16$,

$$\frac{1}{3}\left(I - \frac{I}{16}\right) = \frac{5I}{16}$$

567 Conservation of K.E. may not be used here as a living body can create K.E., chemical energy being changed into K.E. by the muscles.

568 Since the impulses at the axles do not act along the line of centres, **2** is false.

569

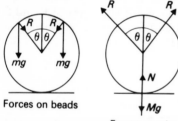

Forces on beads

Forces on wire

$R = mg(2 - 3\cos\theta)$ in the usual way.

The beads produce a vertically upward force F on the wire where $F = 2mg\cos\theta(2 - 3\cos\theta)$ which has maximum value $\frac{2}{3}mg$.

Writing Multiple Choice Items

We have been persuaded to include a section on item writing although we recognize the opposing dangers of stating the obvious and of surrounding the subject with unnecessary mystique.

Good ideas for items often come from the situations which arise in class teaching; textbooks and magazines are also valuable sources of material. Points to have in mind are :

1 A concise, clear statement of the central problem, which can be quickly appreciated, is even more desirable in objective tests than in conventional examinations.

2 Words should not be included in the options which could have been included in the stem.

3 The letters A, B, C, D, E should not appear in the stem, being reserved for use as the labels of the suggested answers.

4 If a question contains a good idea but is proving troublesome, changing the item type can help.

In a Simple Multiple Choice item the problem should normally be posed within the stem : reading responses should not be necessary in order to understand it. The use of an incomplete statement, to be completed by the key, can help towards word economy. Distractors should be plausible and should arise from common mistakes, those arising from a single mistake being preferable to those depending on a multiplicity of errors. A conventional examination can be the source of an item, the wrong answers obtained by candidates being used as distractors. Options should be arranged in logical order if there is one. A question such as **20**, requiring the ordering of three objects or expressions, has the advantage that the five orders other than the given one provide the key and distractors.

Multiple Completion items may be found easier to write than Simple Multiple Choice ones. The difficulty of finding suitable distractors is not encountered and an inspection of our Multiple Completion items will show the variety of different uses to which this item type can be put. It will be noted that the directions do not (and indeed could not) allow for all combinations of true/false answers and that sometimes answering two of the three parts is sufficient to determine the key. However, by judiciously ordering the responses, the writer can ensure that the solver has to come to a decision on those parts which the writer thinks most important. The responses should not be dependent on each other or contradict each other.

123

Ideas for Relationship Analysis items come easily and these items test aspects of mathematics not often tested in conventional examinations. It is important to include sufficient items with key **E**.

Data Necessity items have given us the most trouble. Ideally none of the pieces of information should obviously be necessary but this is not easy to achieve and we have not always succeeded in doing so. The standard of difficulty of these items needs careful consideration for those which are not too obvious are often too involved. Topics in mechanics are most suitable for those starting to write items of this type.

Particular care is needed in writing Data Sufficiency items, especially in mechanics and where real life situations are involved. Any unintentional failure to include all necessary data and any unspecified underlying assumption will make the key **E**. The facts and statements **1** and **2** must be mutually consistent. The statements may be equivalent to each other, when the key will be either **A** or **E**. The stem must not imply either fact (say **1**) or the solver may have difficulty in deciding whether he is using **2** ALONE to solve the problem.

Having written items put them aside for a time. On returning to them it will usually be found that they have deteriorated in quality and increased in difficulty ! Most of our items underwent several stages of refinement, yet still, months after the initial writing, improvements could be made. It is almost essential to have items and explanations of distractors reviewed by a second person who may spot flaws, suggest improvements in wording and distractors, and sometimes see that another item type better suits the idea. Preferably the reviewer should not know the key—the result can be salutary.

Index

1	2	3	
✓		✓	A
✓	✓	✓	B
X	✓	✓	C
✓	X	X	D
X	X	✓	E

RA

1 → 2	2 ≠ 1	A
2 → 1	1 → 2	B
1 ↔ 2		C
1 denies 2	2 denies 1	D
None of these		E

DN

1 not needed	A
2 not needed	B
3 not needed	C
4 not needed	D
All needed	E

DS

1 alone, not 2 alone	A
1 alone, not 2 alone	B
2 alone, not 1 alone	C
1 and 2 together	D
1 and 2 insufficient	E